Macfarlane

APPLIED MATHEMATICS SERIES

Edited by

I. S. SOKOLNIKOFF

MATHEMATICS

OF

RELATIVITY

APPLIED MATHEMATICS SERIES

THE APPLIED MATHEMATICS SERIES is devoted to books dealing with mathematical theories underlying physical and biological sciences, and with advanced mathematical techniques needed for solving problems of these sciences.

THE SERIES provides an outlet for books in the following categories:

(a) Brief introductory monographs on an advanced level.

(b) Treatises concerned with extended coverage of specialized topics.

(c) Advanced textbooks on subjects essential in the study of applied mathematics.

MATHEMATICS

OF

RELATIVITY

G. Y. RAINICH

PROFESSOR OF MATHEMATICS

UNIVERSITY OF MICHIGAN

NEW YORK · JOHN WILEY & SONS, INC.

LONDON · CHAPMAN & HALL, LIMITED

1950

PRINTED IN THE UNITED STATES OF AMERICA

PREFACE

It is my conviction that complete clarity in presenting the theory of relativity can be achieved only by stressing the mathematical aspect of the subject. (The choice of the title of the book reflects this conviction.) It would be possible, as indicated in the Conclusion, first to build the mathematical apparatus and then to show how the theory is interpreted in physical terms. Instead, a different plan of presentation is followed in the text. We begin with the discussion of the familiar subject of the inverse square law in terms of simple calculus and then introduce step by step more complicated situations, gradually bringing in more sophisticated mathematical tools. Both changes in fundamental concepts, which characterize the theory of relativity, and the refinements of the mathematical technique are introduced only as need for them arises. In this way it is attempted to make the presentation easier not by sacrificing rigor but by separating the difficulties, by introducing them one by one.

Most of the material in the book has appeared in one form or another in periodicals and books by other authors. All the main ideas, of course, are due to Einstein and Minkowski. But I have tried to arrange the material in such a way that the theory appears as a consistent whole.

In one important point the theory presented in this book goes beyond earlier work. Since the general relativity theory was first proposed by Einstein it has been thought that, although it takes care of phenomena interpreted earlier in terms of gravitational forces, it fails to account for electromagnetic phenomena. Several generalizations of curved space have been proposed as the basis of a theory which would accommodate electromagnetism as well as gravitation. However, in section 19 of this book it is proved that gravitation together with electromagnetism fits exactly into the original theory of curved space. This means that it is not necessary to generalize it for that purpose. (It does *not* mean, of course, that there cannot be another theory, generalizing the present one, that would be superior to it; for instance, a theory comprising quantum phenomena in addition to gravitation and electromagnetism; it cannot be denied a priori that some more or less plausible generalization of the theory of curved space-time could serve as the basis for such a theory.)

In keeping with the purpose of the book, which is to give a consistent and clear presentation of the theory of relativity in as simple a form as is consistent with the clarity of the fundamental concepts, no attempt is made to cover the literature with any degree of completeness. As a consequence, the reader should not be surprised that certain aspects that are not necessary for the consistent presentation of the basic theory have been omitted. The variational principles, for instance, are not made use of; the cosmological theories are left out; and the paradoxes that result from attempts to adopt the new theory without discarding the so-called common-sense concepts that contradict it are given silent treatment.

I have been teaching a course on the mathematics of relativity in the Mathematics Department of the University of Michigan for more than twenty years, and the book is largely the outcome of that course. An earlier form of it was published as lithoprinted Lecture Notes.

I feel deeply indebted to Professor I. S. Sokolnikoff of the University of California at Los Angeles for the invitation to publish the book as one of the volumes of the series of which he is the editor, and for much-needed encouragement during the preparation of the manuscript.

Thanks are due to Professor Charles L. Dolph of the University of Michigan, who read the next to the last draft of the manuscript and made many helpful suggestions that resulted in a great improvement of the presentation.

G. Y. RAINICH

12 June 1950

CONTENTS

1

OLD PHYSICS

The purpose of this chapter is to reformulate some of the fundamental equations of mechanics and electrodynamics—specifically, to write them in a new form appropriate for the discussion that follows. The content of the chapter is *classical;* the modifications which are characteristic of the relativity theory have not been introduced, but the form is decidedly new.

1. Motion of a particle.   The inverse square law

The fundamental equations of mechanics of a particle are usually written in the form

1.1 $$m \frac{d^2x}{dt^2} = X, \qquad m \frac{d^2y}{dt^2} = Y, \qquad m \frac{d^2z}{dt^2} = Z.$$

Here m denotes the mass of the particle; x, y, z are functions of the time t, whose values are the coordinates of the particles at the corresponding time; and X, Y, Z are functions of the coordinates whose values are the components of the force at the corresponding point. This system of equations was the first example of what we may call mathematical physics, and much that is *now* mathematical physics may be conveniently considered a result of a development whose germ is the system 1.1.   This chapter will be devoted to tracing out some lines of this development.

We begin by writing equations 1.1 in the form

1.11 $$\frac{dmu}{dt} = X, \qquad \frac{dmv}{dt} = Y, \qquad \frac{dmw}{dt} = Z,$$

where

1.2 $$u = \frac{dx}{dt}, \qquad v = \frac{dy}{dt}, \qquad w = \frac{dz}{dt}$$

are the velocity components.   The quantities

$$mu, \qquad mv, \qquad mw$$

are called the momentum components, and in this form our fundamental equations express the statement that the time rate of change
of the momentum is equal to the force, the original statement of Newton.   Equations 1.11 are seen to be equivalent to 1.1 if we use the
notation 1.2 and the fact, usually tacitly assumed, that the mass of a
particle does not change with time, or, in symbols, that

1.12 $$\frac{dm}{dt} = 0.$$

In equations 1.1, x, y, z are usually *unknown* functions of the time,
and X, Y, Z are *given* functions of the coordinates.   The situation
then is this: first the field has to be described by giving the forces
X, Y, Z, and then the motion in the given field is determined by solving
equations 1.1 (with some additional initial conditions).

We shall first discuss fields of a certain simple type.   One of the
simplest fields of force is the so-called inverse square field.   The field
has a center, which is a singularity of the field; in it the field is not
determined.   In every other point of the field the force is directed
toward the center (or away from it), and the magnitude of the force
is inversely proportional to the square of the distance from the center.
As the most common realization of such a field of force we may consider the gravitational field produced by a mass particle.   If cartesian
coordinates with the origin at the particle are introduced, the force
components are

1.3 $$X = \frac{cx}{r^3}, \qquad Y = \frac{cy}{r^3}, \qquad Z = \frac{cz}{r^3}.$$

Here r is the distance of the moving particle from the origin, so
that

1.4 $$r^2 = x^2 + y^2 + z^2,$$

and c is a coefficient of proportionality, negative when we have attrac-
tion and positive when we have repulsion (c depends on the mass of
the particle producing the field and also on the mass of the particle
on which the field acts, but at present we are not interested in these
dependences).   In order to show that 1.3 actually represents the
inverse square law we form the sum of the squares of the components
and find the result to be c^2/r^4, so that the magnitude of the force is
c/r^2.   If the field is produced by several attracting particles the force

at every point (outside of the points where the particles are located) is considered to be given by the sum of the forces due to the separate particles. In these circumstances the expressions become quite complicated, and it is easier to study the general properties of such fields by using certain differential equations to which the force components are subjected rather than by studying the explicit expressions.

These differential equations are as follows:

1.51
$$\frac{\partial X}{\partial x} + \frac{\partial Y}{\partial y} + \frac{\partial Z}{\partial z} = 0,$$

1.52
$$\frac{\partial Y}{\partial z} - \frac{\partial Z}{\partial y} = 0, \quad \frac{\partial Z}{\partial x} - \frac{\partial X}{\partial z} = 0, \quad \frac{\partial X}{\partial y} - \frac{\partial Y}{\partial x} = 0.$$

The fact that the functions X, Y, Z, given by formulas 1.3, satisfy these equations may be proved by direct substitution. To facilitate calculation we may notice that differentiation of 1.4 gives

1.6
$$r \frac{\partial r}{\partial x} = x, \quad r \frac{\partial r}{\partial y} = y, \quad r \frac{\partial r}{\partial z} = z.$$

Differentiating the first of equations 1.3, we have now

$$\frac{\partial X}{\partial x} = \frac{c}{r^3} - 3 \frac{cx}{r^4} \frac{\partial r}{\partial x} = \frac{c}{r^3} - 3 \frac{cx^2}{r^5}.$$

Substituting this and two analogous expressions into 1.51 we easily verify it. The verification of 1.52 presents little difficulty.

It is known that equations 1.52 state a necessary and sufficient condition for the existence of a function ϕ of which X, Y, Z are partial derivatives. The derivative $\partial X/\partial x$ is then the second derivative of this function, and the system 1.51–1.52 may be replaced by the equivalent system

1.53
$$X = \frac{\partial \phi}{\partial x}, \qquad Y = \frac{\partial \phi}{\partial y}, \qquad Z = \frac{\partial \phi}{\partial z}$$

1.54
$$\frac{\partial^2 \phi}{\partial x^2} + \frac{\partial^2 \phi}{\partial y^2} + \frac{\partial^2 \phi}{\partial z^2} = 0.$$

The last equation is known as the equation of Laplace.

In the particular case where X, Y, Z are given by the formulas 1.3, a function ϕ of which X, Y, Z are partial derivatives is (as it is easy to verify)

$$\phi = -\frac{c}{r}.$$

We may say now that the field of force given by 1.3 satisfies the differential equations 1.51–1.52 (or 1.53–1.54, which express the same thing). We will show now that these equations are satisfied not only by the field due to one particle at the origin but also by that due to any number of particles: First, we notice that if a particle is not at the origin this results only in additive constants in the coordinates and so does not affect partial derivatives which appear in the equations 1.51–1.52; these equations therefore remain true. Second, these equations are linear and homogeneous, as a consequence of which the sum of two solutions of these equations necessarily is a solution; hence if two fields satisfy these equations their sum also satisfies them. If, then, as is generally assumed, the field produced by several particles is the sum of the fields due to the individual particles, such a field also satisfies equations 1.51–1.52.

Conversely, it can be proved that any field satisfying the differential equations 1.51–1.52 may be produced by a finite, or infinite, set of particles each of which acts according to the inverse square law. We shall not prove this fact here (the proof is given in potential theory), but we shall show that these equations furnish us the inverse square law again, if we add the condition that the field is symmetric with respect to one point.

A similar situation where we have to solve a system of partial differential equations with the "additional condition" of symmetry will appear again in Chapter 5, and in order to be clear about its significance it is desirable to treat this special case in detail here.

The situation is this: We have a vector field, that is, we are given at each point P a vector v_P, and we know that this field must not be affected by any rigid motion which does not affect a fixed point, namely the origin. In other words, if a rotation around the origin brings a point P into a point Q it must bring the vector v_P into the vector v_Q. Consider first a rotation around the axis OP. This rotation does not affect P. Therefore it must not affect the vector v_P; this can be true only if the vector v_P lies on the axis of rotation OP. The components X, Y, Z of v_P must therefore be proportional to the coordinates x, y, z of the point P, so that we can write

1.7 $X = \lambda x, \qquad Y = \lambda y, \qquad Z = \lambda z.$

The proportionality factor λ may, of course, vary from point to point so that it is a function of the coordinates. Consider now a rotation that brings P into a point Q. Since this rotation brings v_P into v_Q these two vectors must have the same magnitude so that the quantity $\lambda^2(x^2 + y^2 + z^2) = \lambda^2 r^2$ must not be affected by the rotation; in other words, it must be the same for all points which can be brought into each other by a rotation around the origin, that is for all points which are at the same distance r from the origin. This means that $\lambda^2 r^2$, and therefore λ, can depend on r only. We have thus arrived at the result that to satisfy the condition of symmetry a vector field must be of the form 1.7, where λ is a function of r, and it is obvious that any field of this form is symmetric with respect to the origin.

Next, we must impose the requirement that it satisfies the differential equations 1.51–1.52. Since $r\, \partial r/\partial x = x$, so that $\partial r/\partial x = x/r$, etc., we have

$$\frac{\partial X}{\partial x} = \lambda + \lambda' \cdot \frac{x^2}{r}, \qquad \frac{\partial X}{\partial y} = \lambda' \cdot \frac{xy}{r}, \qquad \frac{\partial X}{\partial z} = \lambda' \cdot \frac{xz}{r};$$

$$\frac{\partial Y}{\partial x} = \lambda' \cdot \frac{xy}{r}, \qquad \frac{\partial Y}{\partial y} = \lambda + \lambda' \cdot \frac{y^2}{r}, \qquad \frac{\partial Y}{\partial z} = \lambda' \cdot \frac{yz}{r};$$

$$\frac{\partial Z}{\partial x} = \lambda' \cdot \frac{xz}{r}, \qquad \frac{\partial Z}{\partial y} = \lambda' \cdot \frac{yz}{r}, \qquad \frac{\partial Z}{\partial z} = \lambda + \lambda' \cdot \frac{z^2}{r};$$

where a prime denotes differentiation with respect to r. We see that equations 1.52 do not impose a new restriction on λ. But equation 1.51 gives

$$3\lambda + \lambda' \cdot \frac{x^2 + y^2 + z^2}{r} = 0$$

or

$$\frac{3}{r} + \frac{\lambda'}{\lambda} = 0.$$

Hence $\lambda r^3 = c$, where c is a constant. Substituting $\lambda = c/r^3$ into 1.7 we get 1.3.

Exercise. Derive the result obtained in text by using the potential ϕ.

We see that the general equations 1.51–1.52 give all the general information we need about the fields of force in question; we shall call this system the system of equations of a Newtonian field or simply the *Newtonian system*, although Newton never considered the differential equations that make it up.

We may comment briefly on the mathematical character of the magnitudes and equations we have been dealing with in this section. At every point the quantities X, Y, Z may be considered as the components of a vector, the force vector; we have thus a vector at every point of space, and this constitutes a vector *field*. The function ϕ is an example of a *scalar field*. These two fields are related in a particular way; namely, the first is derived from the second by differentiation. The vector field satisfies equation 1.51, the left-hand member of which is called *divergence* of the vector field. To find a divergence of a vector field we form the sum of the derivatives of the components with respect to the corresponding coordinates. The formula for the divergence may be written more compactly by setting

1.71 $$x = x_1, \qquad y = x_2, \qquad z = x_3,$$

and writing the vector components as

1.72 $$x = X_1, \qquad Y = X_2, \qquad Z = X_3.$$

The expression for the divergence then becomes

1.8 $$\sum_{i=1}^{3} \frac{\partial x_i}{\partial X_i}.$$

The operation of forming the divergence of a vector field is of fundamental importance for our subsequent development.

We now leave the study of force fields temporarily and direct our attention to the left-hand members of the equations of motion.

2. Two pictures of matter

Our fundamental equations 1.1 connect matter, as represented by the left-hand members, with forces, as represented by the right-hand members. There seems to be a fundamental difference in the mathematical aspects of matter and force. The quantities characterizing matter, the momentum components, for example, are functions of one variable t and satisfy *ordinary* differential equations, whereas quantities X, Y, Z, characterizing force, are functions of three variables x, y, z and, as a consequence, are subjected to *partial* differential equations. The force components are *field* quantities, whereas the matter components are not. Another way of putting this is to say that force seems to be distributed *continuously* through space whereas matter is connected with *discrete points*. However, this distinction is not as essential as it looks; it is merely the result of the point of view we take. We could very well consider matter to be distributed continuously through space. Each of the two theories, the discrete theory, according to which matter consists of material points each of which carries a finite mass, and the continuous theory, according to which matter is distributed continuously through space, may be considered as the limiting case of the other. We may start with material points, then increase their number, at the same time decreasing the mass of each, and so approximate with any degree of precision a given continuous distribution.   Or we may start with a continuous distribution, then make the density decrease everywhere except in the constantly decreasing neighborhoods of a discrete number of points, and thus approximate, with any precision, a given discrete distribution.   It is clear that there cannot be any question as to which of the two theories is correct.   Since the difference between them can be made as small as we please, the predictions based on the two theories can be made to agree as closely as we may wish; and, hence, if one identification is successful within experimental error, the other will be likewise. Mathematically the difference will be largely that between ordinary differential equations, which are used in treating the motion of discrete particles, and partial differential equations, which apply to continuous distributions.

We may remark here that, although forces are usually considered to be continuously distributed in space, it is possible to introduce a discrete picture here also.   This is actually being done sometimes in the electromagnetic theory when a field of force is represented by discrete lines of force and the intensity is characterized by the number of lines per square inch.   We shall not, however, have occasion to use this picture.

In quantum mechanics still a third point of view is taken which, in a way, occupies an intermediate position.   Mathematically the treatment is that used in the continuous case (partial differential equations), but the interpretation is given in terms of discrete particles, the continuous quantities being considered as probabilities of a particle being within a certain volume, and the like.   This point of view also will not be used in what follows but is mentioned here for the sake of completeness.

We now wish to describe motion using the continuous picture of matter.   We may begin by introducing a vector u, v, w which represents the velocity observed at a given point at a given time.   Using the terminology introduced in the preceding section we shall speak of a vector field.   And since this vector field depends also on time, u, v, w are functions of the coordinates and the time, which we may write as

$$u(x, y, z, t), \qquad v(x, y, z, t), \qquad w(x, y, z, t).$$

The connection between this vector and the velocity vector considered in the preceding section is established by considering it as the velocity of the particle of the fluid which at the instant t happens to be at the point x, y, z.

Instead of the mass of a particle m we have here the concept of density ρ; this is a function of x, y, z, t, and may be described as a variable scalar field.

The connection between mass and density may be described in this way: using the discrete picture, we may speak of the mass contained in a certain volume at a certain time, meaning by this the sum of the masses of particles which happen to be at that moment in that volume; if there are many particles of small masses this sum may be approximated by the integral of the density $\rho(x,\ y,\ z,\ t)\ dx\ dy\ dz$ over the volume.

The equations of motion of a fluid were given by Euler. We will write them as

$$\frac{\partial \rho uu}{\partial x} + \frac{\partial \rho uv}{\partial y} + \frac{\partial \rho uw}{\partial z} + \frac{\partial \rho u}{\partial t} - \frac{\partial p}{\partial x} = \xi,$$

$$\frac{\partial \rho uv}{\partial x} + \frac{\partial \rho vv}{\partial y} + \frac{\partial \rho vw}{\partial z} + \frac{\partial \rho v}{\partial t} - \frac{\partial p}{\partial y} = \eta,$$

$$\frac{\partial \rho uw}{\partial x} + \frac{\partial \rho vw}{\partial y} + \frac{\partial \rho ww}{\partial z} + \frac{\partial \rho w}{\partial t} - \frac{\partial p}{\partial z} = \zeta.$$

Here p which, like ρ, is a variable scalar field, that is a function of x, y, z, t, denotes *pressure*. It is sometimes connected with forces that act between the particles of the fluid. The quantities ξ, η, ζ bear about the same relation to the force components X, Y, Z as the density bears to mass. The vector ξ, η, ζ is called the force per unit volume. If in the discrete picture we consider the sum F of the forces (*external* forces, as distinct from the internal forces produced by other particles) acting at the moment t on all the particles within a certain volume, and consider a continuous approximation, then the integrals $\int \xi\ dx\ dy\ dz$, $\int \eta\ dx\ dy\ dz$, $\int \zeta\ dx\ dy\ dz$ will approximate the components of F at the time t.

The above equations correspond to equations 1.11 and could be derived from them, under certain assumptions, by considering the fluid as the limit of a set of particles; also the Newtonian equations may be considered as a limiting case of Euler's equations by passing to the limit as indicated at the beginning of this section. However, we will not give these derivations here and will feel free to pass from one picture of matter to the other and replace the ordinary differential equations by the partial differential equations, and vice versa. In addition to equations 1.11 we had also equation 1.12, which states (for matter distributed discretely) that the mass of a particle does **not** change with time.   For continuous distribution of matter the corresponding equation is

$$\frac{\partial \rho u}{\partial x} + \frac{\partial \rho v}{\partial y} + \frac{\partial \rho w}{\partial z} + \frac{\partial \rho}{\partial t} = 0.$$

This equation is called the *continuity equation of matter*.

We will conclude this section by commenting on the mathematical structure of these equations.   We have already introduced the notation x_1, x_2, x_3 for the coordinates; it seems natural to write also u_1, u_2, u_3 for the velocity components instead of u, v, w.   With this notation the first three terms of the continuity equation can be written analogously to equation 1.8, as $\sum\limits_{i=1}^{3} \dfrac{\partial \rho u_i}{\partial x_i}$; and we may include the fourth term by writing $t = x_4$, setting $u_4 = 1$, and allowing the index of summation i to range from 1 to 4.   Then the continuity equation assumes the simple form

$$\sum_{i=1}^{4} \frac{\partial \rho u_i}{\partial x_i} = 0.$$

The Euler equations when written in this new notation exhibit a striking symmetry; they assume the form

$$\sum_{j=1}^{4} \frac{\partial \rho u_i u_j}{\partial x_j} - \frac{\partial p}{\partial x_i} = \xi_i \quad (i = 1, 2, 3).$$

Here, of course, ξ_i stands for ξ, η, ζ, depending on the value of the index i.

The fact that we have numbered our independent variables permits us to introduce a further simplification into our notation.   We may write the differential operators $\partial/\partial x$, $\partial/\partial y$, $\partial/\partial z$, $\partial/\partial t$ as ∂_i, for the four different values of the index i, so that the partial derivatives of any function ψ can be written as

$$\partial_i \psi = \frac{\partial \psi}{\partial x_i}.$$

With these notational simplifications the Euler equations become

$$2.1 \qquad \sum_{j=1}^{4} \partial_j(\rho u_i u_j) - \partial_i p = \xi_i \quad (i = 1, 2, 3),$$

and the continuity equation becomes

2.2
$$\sum_{i=1}^{4} \partial_i(\rho u_i) = 0.$$

The sums in the last two equations appear as generalizations of what we called divergence in the preceding section. We shall continue calling them divergences, and will make a closer study of the structure of these and related expressions in the next section.

3. Vectors, tensors, operations

We shall treat the fundamental concepts of vector and tensor analysis in a systematic way in section 10. At present we shall show how the language of this theory, which for ordinary space has been partly introduced in section 1, can be applied to the case of four independent variables and extended so as to furnish a simple way of describing the relations introduced in the preceding section.

A quantity like ρ or p which depends on the independent variables x, y, z, t we shall call a *scalar* field. The four quantities u_1, u_2, u_3, u_4 we shall consider as the components of a *vector*. (If we want to emphasize that these quantities depend on x, y, z, t, we will speak of a *vector field*.) The sixteen quantities $\rho u_i u_j$ furnish an example of a *tensor* (or tensor field). A convenient way to arrange the components of a tensor is in a square array, for instance:

3.1
$$\begin{array}{cccc}
\rho u_1 u_1 & \rho u_1 u_2 & \rho u_1 u_3 & \rho u_1 u_4 \\
\rho u_2 u_1 & \rho u_2 u_2 & \rho u_2 u_3 & \rho u_2 u_4 \\
\rho u_3 u_1 & \rho u_3 u_2 & \rho u_3 u_3 & \rho u_3 u_4 \\
\rho u_4 u_1 & \rho u_4 u_2 & \rho u_4 u_3 & \rho u_4 u_4.
\end{array}$$

We also obtain a tensor if we differentiate each of the components of a vector with respect to each of the variables x, y, z, t, for instance:

3.2
$$\begin{array}{cccc}
\partial_1 u_1 & \partial_2 u_1 & \partial_3 u_1 & \partial_4 u_1 \\
\partial_1 u_2 & \partial_2 u_2 & \partial_3 u_2 & \partial_4 u_2 \\
\partial_1 u_3 & \partial_2 u_3 & \partial_3 u_3 & \partial_4 u_3 \\
\partial_1 u_4 & \partial_2 u_4 & \partial_3 u_4 & \partial_4 u_4.
\end{array}$$

A very important tensor is one whose array is given by

3.4
$$\begin{array}{cccc}
1 & 0 & 0 & 0 \\
0 & 1 & 0 & 0 \\
0 & 0 & 1 & 0 \\
0 & 0 & 0 & 1.
\end{array}$$

It may be described by saying that its components in the main diagonal are all ones and the off-diagonal components are zero. These components are usually denoted by δ_{ij} so that δ_{ij} has the value *one* if the indices have the same value and *zero* if i and j are distinct; δ_{ij} is often referred to as the *Kronecker symbol*. Using these symbols we can further simplify the writing of the Euler equations. In order to do that we notice that $\partial_i p$ may be written $\sum\limits_{j=1}^{4} \delta_{ij}\, \partial_j p$ since the terms in this sum for which j is different from i are zero because the first factor is zero according to the definition of δ_{ij}; and in the remaining term, the one in which $j = i$, the first factor by the same definition is equal to 1. Equations 2.1 may therefore be written

$$\sum_{j=1}^{4} \partial_j(\rho u_i u_j) - \sum_{j=1}^{4} \delta_{ij}\partial_j p = \xi_i,$$

or

$$\sum_{j=1}^{4} \partial_j(\rho u_i u_j - \delta_{ij} p) = \xi_i,$$

or finally, introducing the notation

3.5 $$M_{ij} = \rho u_i u_j - \delta_{ij} p,$$

as

3.6 $$\sum_{j=1}^{4} \partial_j M_{ij} = \xi_i \qquad (i = 1, 2, 3).$$

Since the components M_{ij} are obtained by combining quantities connected with matter, namely, density, velocity, and pressure, the tensor M_{ij} is called the *tensor of matter*.

Let us stop and summarize what we have been doing. Earlier we obtained a tensor by differentiating the components of a vector. When we write $\partial_i p$ we obtain from a scalar the components of a vector (this vector is called the gradient of the scalar p). We obtained the tensor M_{ij} by first multiplying the tensors ρu_i and u_j, then subtracting from the result the product of the tensors p and δ_{ij}. We indicated above how a tensor can be obtained from a vector by differentiating its components; similarly we may differentiate the components of a tensor: for instance, by differentiating each of the 16 components, M_{ij}, of the tensor introduced above with respect to each of the independent variables x_k we obtain 16×4 numbers (or functions) $\partial_k M_{ij}$.

These numbers are denoted by symbols with three indices. In general, we shall consider such symbols as the components of a tensor of *rank three;* what we have so far called a tensor we shall now call more precisely a tensor of *rank two.* If we call a vector a tensor of rank one, and a scalar a tensor of rank zero, etc., we may say that the operation of differentiation leads from a tensor (or, better, a tensor field) to a tensor of the next higher rank.

The above discussion of the continuity equation furnishes us an example of still another operation on tensors, namely contraction: From the tensor of rank one, viz., ρu_i, we can obtain by differentiation the tensor of rank two, viz., $\partial_j(\rho u_i)$. The left member of the continuity equation is nothing but the sum of those components of this tensor which have two equal indices. This operation of forming the sum of those components of a tensor of rank two which have equal indices is called *contraction;* it leads from a tensor of rank two to a scalar, i.e., a tensor of rank zero. If the components of a tensor of rank two are arranged in an array we can also say that contraction is the forming of the sum of the diagonal terms.

The operation of contraction can be applied further to a tensor of rank higher than the second; to contract with respect to two indices, say k and j, means to form the sums of components in which these two indices have the same value. From the tensor of rank three, $\partial_k M_{ij}$, by contracting with respect to k and j, we obtain the tensor of rank one $\sum_{j=1}^{4} \partial_j M_{ij}$ which appears as the left member of equations 3.6.

As the operation of contraction will be performed very often it is convenient to simplify our notation still further by omitting the symbol of summation. This is possible because it very seldom is necessary to consider an expression with two equal indices (represented by letters) without having to form a sum (the situation never occurs in this book). We therefore *agree when we write a symbol with two equal indices to consider it as meaning that we must form the sum of all terms obtained from it by giving to these indices the values 1, 2, 3, and 4,* or from 1 to n if it is clear what n is.

Equations 3.6 and 2.2 will therefore now be written as

$$\partial_j M_{ij} = \xi_i$$

and

$$\partial_i(\rho u_i) = 0,$$

respectively. The first gives an example of the divergence of a tensor; the second, of the divergence of a vector.

Some familiar situations in which the operation of contraction is used are as follows. The formation of the scalar product of two vectors u_i and v_i may be considered as resulting from their multiplication followed by contraction: the multiplication gives the tensor of the second rank $u_i v_j$; contracting this we get $u_i v_i = u_1 v_1 + u_2 v_2 + u_3 v_3$, which is the inner product; the inner product of two vectors could also be called the contracted product of the two vectors. In an analogous fashion we can form a contracted product of two tensors of the second rank. If the tensors are a_{ij} and b_{ij} the contracted product will be $a_{ik} b_{kj}$; it is also a tensor of rank two. It may be interesting to note that the formation of the contracted product of two tensors is essentially the same operation as that involved in the multiplying of two determinants corresponding to the arrays representing the tensors; to see that, it will be enough to consider two three-row determinants

$$\begin{vmatrix} a_{11} & a_{12} & a_{13} \\ a_{21} & a_{22} & a_{23} \\ a_{31} & a_{32} & a_{33} \end{vmatrix} \quad \text{and} \quad \begin{vmatrix} b_{11} & b_{12} & b_{13} \\ b_{21} & b_{22} & b_{23} \\ b_{31} & b_{32} & b_{33} \end{vmatrix}.$$

Their product, according to the theorem of multiplication of determinants, is

$$\begin{vmatrix} a_{11}b_{11} + a_{12}b_{21} + a_{13}b_{31} & a_{11}b_{12} + a_{12}b_{22} + a_{13}b_{32} & a_{11}b_{13} + a_{12}b_{23} + a_{13}b_{33} \\ a_{21}b_{11} + a_{22}b_{21} + a_{23}b_{31} & a_{21}b_{12} + a_{22}b_{22} + a_{23}b_{32} & a_{21}b_{13} + a_{22}b_{23} + a_{23}b_{33} \\ a_{31}b_{11} + a_{32}b_{21} + a_{33}b_{31} & a_{31}b_{12} + a_{22}b_{22} + a_{33}b_{32} & a_{31}b_{13} + a_{32}b_{23} + a_{33}b_{33} \end{vmatrix},$$

and it is seen that the elements of this determinant are the components of the tensor of rank two which arises from the tensor a_{ij} and b_{ij} by first multiplying them and then contracting with respect to the two inside indices.

4. Maxwell's equations

In section 1 we discussed from a formal point of view the inverse square law and the fields of a more general nature that can be derived from it; and we expressed the laws of these fields in terms of three-dimensional tensor analysis, i.e., we employed only three independent variables; after that we found that matter is best discussed (from the continuous point of view) by using four-dimensional tensor analysis. We have thus a discrepancy: two different mathematical tools are used in the treatment of the two sides of the fundamental equations of mechanics. This discrepancy will be removed in what follows. It will be removed by considering force fields that differ from those derived by composition of inverse square laws, by modifying, in a sense, this law. However, the modifications will be different for the two types of field for which the inverse square law has been applied in older physics, namely the gravitational and the electromagnetic.

Originally, the inverse square law was introduced in the time of Newton in application to gravitational forces; in Chapter 5 we shall discuss the gravitational phenomena and see what modifications— radical in nature, but very slight as far as numerical values are concerned—the inverse square law will undergo. Later, it was recognized that the inverse square law applied also to the electrostatic and magnetostatic fields produced by one single electric or magnetic particle, respectively. Still later a more general law for electromagnetic fields was introduced by Faraday and Maxwell. This we shall study now.

If X, Y, Z denote the components of electric force in the static symmetric case, as just mentioned, the inverse square law applies, and, as shown in section 1, it follows, under the assumption of additivity, that for a field produced by any number of particles the divergence vanishes; that is,

4.1
$$\frac{\partial X}{\partial x} + \frac{\partial Y}{\partial y} + \frac{\partial Z}{\partial z} = 0.$$

The quantities $\partial Y/\partial z - \partial Z/\partial y$, $\partial Z/\partial x - \partial X/\partial z$, $\partial X/\partial y - \partial Y/\partial x$ also vanish. Now, a *static* magnetic field does not interact with the electric field, but when a *changing* magnetic field is present the laws of the electric field are modified; viz., the quantities just mentioned are not zero any more but are proportional or, in appropriately chosen units, equal to the time derivatives of the components L, M, N of the magnetic field, so that in addition to 4.1 we have

4.11
$$\frac{\partial Y}{\partial z} - \frac{\partial Z}{\partial y} = \frac{\partial L}{\partial t},$$

$$\frac{\partial Z}{\partial x} - \frac{\partial X}{\partial z} = \frac{\partial M}{\partial t},$$

$$\frac{\partial X}{\partial y} - \frac{\partial Y}{\partial x} = \frac{\partial N}{\partial t}.$$

These equations constitute a mathematical expression of the physical phenomenon which may be described by saying that a magnetic field which changes in time is accompanied by (or "produces") an electric field. This phenomenon, known as induction, is used, for example, in an electric generator or a magneto where the change of the magnetic field is produced by moving the magnet relative to a conductor (or vice versa) in which an electric field is then produced in the form of an electric current.

In similar fashion, the divergence of the magnetic force vanishes,

$$4.2 \qquad \frac{\partial L}{\partial x} + \frac{\partial M}{\partial y} + \frac{\partial N}{\partial z} = 0,$$

and the expressions $\partial M/\partial z - \partial N/\partial y$, $\partial N/\partial x - \partial L/\partial z$, $\partial L/\partial y - \partial M/\partial x$ are proportional to the time derivatives of the electric components. The factor of proportionality, however, *cannot be reduced to 1.* By an appropriate choice of units it can be reduced to *minus 1,* and no changing of directions or sense of coordinate axes will enable us to eliminate this minus sign without introducing a minus sign in the preceding equations. This minus sign is of *extreme importance* in what follows, as we shall have occasion to observe many times. In the meantime we write out the remaining equations

$$\frac{\partial M}{\partial z} - \frac{\partial N}{\partial y} = - \frac{\partial X}{\partial t},$$

$$4.21 \qquad \frac{\partial N}{\partial x} - \frac{\partial L}{\partial z} = - \frac{\partial Y}{\partial t},$$

$$\frac{\partial L}{\partial y} - \frac{\partial M}{\partial x} = - \frac{\partial Z}{\partial t}.$$

This set of equations gives mathematical expression to the counterpart of the physical phenomenon mentioned above which appears, for instance, when an electric current flows near a magnetic needle. The electric current may be considered as equivalent to a moving electric charge which creates an electric field changing with time, and this produces a magnetic field which is manifested in the motion of the magnetic needle. An electromagnet represents another manifestation of the same phenomenon.

Some expositions make it appear that Maxwell's equations are *derived* from the laws of electromagnetic induction involved in the above phenomena. It would be more illuminating to say that Maxwell *guessed* (by an elaborate process) at the right equations—right in the sense that actually observed phenomena can be derived from them; and not only that, but new phenomena, not yet observed, could be predicted from these equations, and new connections could be foreseen on the basis of them. We mention the prediction of the existence of electromagnetic waves and the establishment of the electromagnetic theory of light, and, in particular, the prediction of the phenomenon of the pressure of light.

The point of view, or the manner of presentation, which places the Maxwell equations at the beginning was introduced by Heinrich Herz (who also played an important part in the experimental investigation of electromagnetic waves). According to this point of view, Maxwell's equations cannot be proved; they have to be regarded as the fundamental equations of a mathematical theory, whose justification lies in the fact that its quantities have been successfully identified with measured quantities of physics; this means that for physical quantities the same relationships have been established experimentally as those deduced for the corresponding theoretical quantities from the fundamental equations. We should note here that the equations as they appear above present a simplified and idealized form of the fundamental equations, namely, the fundamental equations for the case of free space, i.e., complete absence of matter.

The choice of units that made the above simple form possible concerns not only units of electric and magnetic force but also units of length and time; it was necessary to choose them in such a way that the velocity of light, which, in ordinary units, is 300,000 kilometers per second, becomes 1. It is important to note that, if in what follows we speak of the velocity β of an object being, let us say, 0.01, we mean that it has this value in units in which the velocity of light is 1; in other words, the velocity in question is one-hundredth of the velocity of light. To put it still in another way, β is the ratio of the velocity of the object to the velocity of light. As a result of this, ordinary velocities, such as we observe in everyday life, are expressed by very small quantities.

For our purposes it is convenient to arrange our equations in the following form, where differentiation with respect to a variable is indicated by a subscript:

$$N_y - M_z - X_t = 0, \qquad Z_y - Y_z + L_t = 0,$$

$$L_z - N_x - Y_t = 0, \qquad X_z - Z_x + M_t = 0,$$

4.3

$$M_x - L_y - Z_t = 0, \qquad Y_x - X_y + N_t = 0,$$

$$X_x + Y_y + Z_z = 0, \qquad \mathbf{L}_x + M_y + N_z = 0.$$

Exercise. Eliminate from the set of Maxwell equations all but one of the components, for instance X, and note how the "minus-sign trouble" appears in

the resulting second-order equation, called the wave equation. An equation of
the same form appeared also in the old wave theory of light before the introduction
of the electromagnetic theory.

As mentioned before, the above equations describe the behavior of
electric and magnetic forces in free space, that is, in regions where
there is no matter, or where we may neglect matter. On the discrete
theory of matter these equations still hold everywhere except at points
occupied by matter—in this theory matter appears as singularity of
the field, and some numerical characteristics of matter, such as electric
charge, appear as residues corresponding to these singularities. These
singularities and residues are analogous to singularities and residues
in the theory of analytic function of a complex variable. The two
theories, that of analytic functions and that of the electromagnetic
field, are analogous in this definite sense, namely, that they are two
special cases of the same general theory introduced by Volterra as
early as 1889 and developed more recently under the name of harmonic
integrals.* The wave equation discussed in the exercise above is
analogous to the Laplace equation which plays a part in the theory
of analytic functions. We shall not discuss this point of view, although
mathematically it is very interesting.

On the continuous theory some terms that represent matter have
to be added to the preceding equations. The second set of Maxwell's
equations 4.3 remains unaltered, but the first set is modified in that
the left-hand sides no longer vanish but become proportional to the
velocity components of matter. The coefficient of proportionality
is the electric density which we denote by ε. The equations of Maxwell for space with matter are thus

$$4.31 \quad \begin{aligned} N_y - M_z - X_t &= \varepsilon u, & Z_y - Y_z + L_t &= 0, \\ L_z - N_x - Y_t &= \varepsilon v, & X_z - Z_x + M_t &= 0, \\ M_x - L_y - Z_t &= \varepsilon w, & Y_x - X_y + N_t &= 0, \\ X_x + Y_y + Z_z &= \varepsilon, & L_x + M_y + N_z &= 0. \end{aligned}$$

Here we come across a new scalar quantity, electric density. However, in most cases this density is proportional to the mass density ρ
we considered before, where the factor of proportionality is capable of
only two numerical values, one negative for negative electricity, and
the other positive for positive electricity.

* See book by W. V. D. Hodge, *The Theory and Applications of Harmonic
Integrals*, Cambridge University Press, 1941.

Even these equations are not sufficient for the description of electromagnetic phenomena; they correspond to a certain idealization in which the dielectric constant and magnetic permeability are neglected; but we shall not go beyond this idealization.

In the above equations we have four independent variables x, y, z, t, as in the discussion of matter in section 2, and we may try now to apply to them the same notation that has been introduced in that section and section 3. The main question here is how to treat the six quantities X, Y, Z, L, M, N. The question was solved by Minkowski in 1907 in the following way: It is clear that a vector has *too few* components to take care of these quantities. Instead of using two vectors, Minkowski proposed to use a *tensor of rank two*. Of course, a tensor has *too many* components; to be exact, it has, in the general case, sixteen components: four in the main diagonal, six above, and six below. If we set those in the main diagonal zero, and those under the main diagonal equal with opposite sign to those above the main diagonal symmetric to them, we are left with exactly six essentially different components which we may identify with the six components X, Y, Z, L, M, N. The restriction just introduced can be expressed in a single formula

4.4 $$F_{ij} + F_{ij} = 0.$$

In fact, the elements in the main diagonal correspond to equal indices. And if we set $j = i$ the above formula becomes $F_{ii} + F_{ii} = 2F_{ii} = 0$, whence $F_{ii} = 0$, as asserted. We try now to identify the components of this tensor with our electromagnetic force components in the following way:

4.5 $$X = F_{41}, \qquad Y = F_{42}, \qquad Z = F_{43},$$
$$L = F_{23}, \qquad M = F_{31}, \qquad N = F_{12}.$$

Using this notation together with 4.4, which, for example, implies that $F_{14} = -X$, we can write the first set 4.3 in the following highly satisfactory form:

$$\partial_2 F_{12} + \partial_3 F_{13} + \partial_4 F_{14} = 0,$$

4.6
$$\partial_3 F_{23} + \partial_1 F_{21} + \partial_4 F_{24} = 0,$$

$$\partial_1 F_{31} + \partial_2 F_{32} + \partial_4 F_{34} = 0,$$

$$\partial_1 F_{41} + \partial_2 F_{42} + \partial_3 F_{43} = 0,$$

or

$$\partial_i F_{ji} = 0.$$

These four equations show a high degree of symmetry. Moreover, they show a very pronounced similarity to some of the equations we have been considering in section 2, and for which we developed a system of notation in section 3. We can say that the four equations written above express the fact that the divergence of the tensor F_{ij} just introduced vanishes in the case of free space. However, if we apply the same notation to the second set 4.3 of Maxwell's equations nothing very simple results; the minus sign mentioned after formula 4.2 above seems to cause trouble. However, there exists a way out from even this difficulty. It was indicated (before Minkowski's paper) in the work of Poincaré and Marcolongo, and foreshadowed in a private letter by Hamilton as early as 1845. We can overcome the difficulty if we allow ourselves to use imaginary quantities side by side with real quantities. This ought to cause no difficulties provided that we know the formal rules of operations, since our new notation is of an entirely formal nature anyway. We set now, instead of 1.71,

4.7 $\qquad x = x_1, \qquad y = x_2, \qquad z = x_3, \qquad ti = x_4;$

and instead of 4.5,

$$iX = F_{41}, \qquad iY = F_{42}, \qquad iZ = F_{43},$$
4.72
$$L = F_{23}, \qquad M = F_{31}, \qquad N = F_{12};$$

and then the first set 4.3 becomes 4.6 as before, but the second set 4.3 also acquires a highly satisfactory form: namely,

$$\partial_2 F_{43} + \partial_3 F_{24} + \partial_4 F_{32} = 0,$$

$$\partial_1 F_{34} + \partial_3 F_{41} + \partial_4 F_{13} = 0,$$

$$\partial_1 F_{42} + \partial_2 F_{14} + \partial_4 F_{21} = 0,$$

$$\partial_1 F_{23} + \partial_2 F_{31} + \partial_3 F_{12} = 0,$$

or

4.61 $\qquad\qquad \partial_i F_{jk} + \partial_j F_{ik} + \partial_k F_{ij} = 0.$

As mentioned before, we consider the components F_{ij} as the components of a tensor. We may say that we have sixteen of them: the six which appear in relations 4.72; six more which result from them by interchanging the indices and whose values differ from those given in 4.72 only in sign; and four more with equal indices. According to formula 4.4 they are zero. We may arrange them in a square array as follows:

$$4.8 \quad \begin{matrix} F_{11} & F_{12} & F_{13} & F_{14} \\ F_{21} & F_{22} & F_{23} & F_{24} \\ F_{31} & F_{32} & F_{33} & F_{34} \\ F_{41} & F_{42} & F_{43} & F_{44} \end{matrix} \quad \text{or} \quad \begin{matrix} 0 & N & -M & -iX \\ -N & 0 & L & -iY \\ M & -L & 0 & -iZ \\ iX & iY & iZ & 0. \end{matrix}$$

We may compare the property $F_{ij} = -F_{ji}$, which our new tensor has, with the property $M_{ij} = M_{ji}$ possessed by the tensor of matter 2.7 (and which is simply the result of commutativity of multiplication). These two properties are manifested in the square arrays 3.1 and 4.8 in that the components of M_{ij} which are symmetric with respect to the main diagonal are equal, and those of F_{ij} which are symmetric with respect to the main diagonal are opposite. Tensors of the first type are called *symmetric;* those of the second, *antisymmetric,* or skew-symmetric.

It might seem that the introduction of imaginaries which permitted us to write Maxwell's equations in a nice form would spoil the nice form which we previously succeeded in giving to the equations of Euler. However, we notice that, in these equations and in the continuity equation, differentiation with respect to time occurs always in the presence of u_4. It is therefore sufficient to replace the notation $u_4 = 1$ (compare 2.41) by the notation

$$4.9 \qquad u_4 = i$$

in order to compensate for the change of x_4 and thus to preserve the form of these equations.

Now we may consider the Maxwell equations with matter 4.31; the second set is not affected and may be written as 4.61, but the first will appear in a form which may be written simply as

$$4.62 \qquad \partial_i F_{ji} = \varepsilon u_j.$$

Exercise. Prove the equation of continuity of matter as a consequence of these equations.

5. The stress-energy tensor

So far the equations to which we have subjected force components have been linear equations, whereas operations performed on matter involved squares and products of matter components. The similarity that we observed in the mathematical aspects of force and matter components makes it seem desirable to subject force components to operations analogous to those we applied to matter, viz., multiplication.

As it happens, certain quadratic combinations of the quantities

X, Y, Z, L, M, N have been introduced in physics. Maxwell himself, giving a mathematical expression to an idea of Faraday (who conceived the space in which magnetic forces are present as being in a state of tension or stress analogous to that of an elastic medium), introduced what is called magnetic and electric stresses. The expression for the electromagnetic energy also involves squares of the electric and magnetic components. Finally, in his studies of electromagnetic theory of light Poynting introduced a vector which is essentially the vector product of the electric and magnetic vectors.

We return to our notation (1.72) X_1, X_2, X_3 for X, Y, Z and form the tensor X_iX_j. This tensor, slightly modified, plays an important part in the theory. The modification consists in subtracting from it $\frac{1}{2}\delta_{ij}X_kX_k$, where δ_{ij} are the components of the tensor introduced in 3.4 and X_kX_k stands for the contracted square of the vector X_i, i.e., $X^2 + Y^2 + Z^2$. We consider then the tensor

$$S_{ij} = X_iX_j - \tfrac{1}{2}\delta_{ij}X_kX_k$$

whose array is

$$\begin{array}{ccc} \tfrac{1}{2}(X^2 - Y^2 - Z^2) & XY & XZ \\[2mm] XY & \tfrac{1}{2}(Y^2 - X^2 - Z^2) & YZ \\[2mm] XZ & YZ & \tfrac{1}{2}(Z^2 - X^2 - Y^2). \end{array}$$

In order to make the introduction of this tensor appear less artificial we will indicate now a connection between it and certain expressions which we have already encountered. We form the (three-dimensional) divergence ∂_jS_{ij} (where i and j take on values from 1 to 3), or in components

$$X(X_x + Y_y + Z_z) + Y(X_y - Y_x) + Z(X_z - Z_x),$$

$$X(Y_x - X_y) + Y(X_x + Y_y + Z_z) + Z(Y_z - Z_y),$$

$$X(Z_x - X_z) + Y(Z_y - Y_z) + Z(X_x + Y_y + Z_z).$$

The connection of these expressions with the Newtonian equations (1.51–1.52) is obvious; the expressions in brackets are the left-hand sides of the Newtonian equation, so that the divergence of our new tensor $X_iX_j - \frac{1}{2}\delta_{ij}X_kX_k$ vanishes as the result of these equations. This again confirms the fact that from the mathematical point of view force and matter components are of very similar nature. We now have in mind electric and magnetic forces. If X, Y, Z are the components of the electric force vector, the tensor, whose array is written out above, is called the "electric stress tensor." An analogous expression in magnetic components is called the "magnetic stress tensor." The sum of the two, namely,

$$\frac{1}{2}(X^2 + L^2 - Y^2 - Z^2 - M^2 - N^2) \qquad XY + LM \qquad\qquad XZ + LN$$

$$XY + LM \qquad \frac{1}{2}(Y^2 + M^2 - X^2 - Z^2 - L^2 - N^2) \qquad YZ + MN$$

$$XZ + LN \qquad\qquad YZ + MN \qquad \frac{1}{2}(Z^2 + N^2 - X^2 - Y^2 - L^2 - M^2),$$

is the tensor introduced by Maxwell under the name "electromagnetic stress tensor." It plays some part in electromagnetic theory, for instance in the discussion of light pressure, but its main applications and importance seem to be in the study of the fundamental questions, as part of a more general four-dimensional tensor.

We saw how nicely the system of indices worked in Maxwell's equations. It is natural to express in index notation the electromagnetic stress tensor also. We assert that the required expression is given by

5.1 $$E_{ij} = F_{ik}F_{kj} - \tfrac{1}{4}\delta_{ij}F_{sk}F_{ks},$$

where i, j take on values 1, 2, 3, and the summations indicated by k and s are extended from 1 to 4. In fact,

$$F_{sk}F_{ks} = F_{12}F_{21} + F_{13}F_{31} + F_{14}F_{41} + F_{21}F_{12} + F_{23}F_{32} + \cdots$$

$$= 2(-L^2 - M^2 - N^2 + X^2 + Y^2 + Z^2),$$

$$F_{1k}F_{k1} = F_{12}F_{21} + F_{13}F_{31} + F_{14}F_{41} = -N^2 - M^2 + X^2,$$

$$E_{11} = F_{1k}F_{k1} - \tfrac{1}{4}F_{sk}F_{ks}$$

$$= -N^2 - M^2 + X^2 + \tfrac{1}{2}L^2 + \tfrac{1}{2}M^2 + \tfrac{1}{2}N^2 - \tfrac{1}{2}X^2 - \tfrac{1}{2}Y^2 - \tfrac{1}{2}Z^2$$

$$= \tfrac{1}{2}(X^2 + L^2 - Y^2 - Z^2 - M^2 - N^2),$$

$$E_{12} = F_{1k}F_{k2} = F_{13}F_{32} + F_{14}F_{42} = LM + XY,$$

and similar expressions for the other components result from the different combinations of the indices, 1 2, 3 for i and j. There seems to be an inconsistency here; the summation indices k and s run from 1 to 4, but only the values 1, 2, 3 are considered for i and j. It is interesting to see the result of letting i and j take on the value 4. We obtain four new components, namely,

$$E_{14} = F_{1k}F_{k4} + F_{12}F_{24} + F_{13}F_{34} = i(NY - MZ),$$

$$E_{24} = F_{2k}F_{k4} + F_{21}F_{14} + F_{23}F_{34} = i(LZ - NX),$$

$$E_{34} = F_{3k}F_{k4} + F_{31}F_{14} + F_{32}F_{24} = i(MX - LY),$$

$$E_{44} = F_{4k}F_{k4} - \tfrac{1}{2}(-L^2 - M^2 - N^2 + X^2 + Y^2 + Z^2)$$

$$= \tfrac{1}{2}(X^2 + Y^2 + Z^2 + L^2 + M^2 + N^2).$$

These quantities happen also to have physical meaning. The first three constitute (except for the factor i) the components of the Poynting vector mentioned above, and the last one is the so-called electromagnetic energy (or energy density). We are thus led by the notation we have introduced in a purely mathematical way to some physical quantities; we may say that the entire tensor with its sixteen components—it is called "the electromagnetic stress-energy tensor"—unifies in a single expression all the second-degree quantities appearing in the electromagnetic theory: the stress components, the Poynting components, and the energy.

The stress-energy tensor may be written out in the form of the following square array:

$$5.2 \quad \begin{array}{cccc} X^2 + L^2 - h & XY + LM & XZ + LN & i(NY - MZ) \\ XY + LM & Y^2 + M^2 - h & YZ + MN & i(LZ - NX) \\ XZ + LM & YZ + MN & Z^2 + N^2 - h & i(MX - LY) \\ i(MZ - NY) & i(NX - LZ) & i(LY - MX) & h \end{array}$$

where

$$5.3 \qquad h = \tfrac{1}{2}(X^2 + Y^2 + Z^2 + L^2 + M^2 + N^2).$$

Exercise 1. Show that the stress-energy tensor is not changed when we substitute for X, Y, Z, L, M, N the expressions

$X \cos \theta - L \sin \theta,$ $X \sin \theta + L \cos \theta,$

$Y \cos \theta - M \sin \theta,$ $Y \sin \theta + M \cos \theta,$

$Z \cos \theta - N \sin \theta,$ $Z \sin \theta + N \cos \theta.$

Exercise 2. Show that the changes of X, Y, Z, L, M, N indicated in the preceding exercise are the only ones that do not affect the stress-energy tensor.

Exercise 3. Introduce the notations $F_{15} = u_1$, $F_{25} = u_2$, $F_{35} = u_3$, $F_{45} = u_5$ and calculate the expression 5.1, letting indices run from 1 to 5.

6. General equations of motion. The complete tensor

We let ourselves be guided once more by what seems to be natural from the formal point of view, and form the (four-dimensional) divergence of the new tensor. This can be done either in components or in index notation. We show how to do it in index notation and leave it to the reader to write out the stress-energy tensor as an array and to form the divergence of the separate lines. Applying formula 3.6 to the tensor 5.1 we have

$$\partial_j E_{ij} = \partial_j F_{ik} \cdot F_{kj} + F_{ik} \cdot \partial_j F_{kj} - \tfrac{1}{4}\delta_{ij}(2F_{sk} \cdot \partial_j F_{ks})$$

$$= \partial_j F_{ik} \cdot F_{kj} + F_{ik}\partial_j F_{kj} + \tfrac{1}{2}F_{ks} \cdot \partial_i F_{ks}$$

The first term on the right may be split up in two equal parts, one of which, writing s for j, may be written as $\tfrac{1}{2}\partial_s F_{ik} \cdot F_{ks}$, and the other takes the form $\tfrac{1}{2}\partial_k F_{si} \cdot F_{ks}$. To obtain it we have written k for j and s for k, and we have interchanged indices in both factors, which does not affect the value because it amounts to changing the sign twice. We thus have

$$\partial_j E_{ij} = \tfrac{1}{2}F_{ks}(\partial_s F_{ik} + \partial_i F_{sk} + \partial_k F_{si}) + F_{ik} \cdot \partial_j F_{kj}.$$

Substituting for the second factors their values from Maxwell's equations 4.61 and 4.62 (in space with matter) we get

$$\partial_j E_{ij} = F_{ik} u_k,$$

or in components without indices

6.1
$$\partial_j E_{1j} = \varepsilon(Nv - Mw + X),$$
$$\partial_j E_{2j} = \varepsilon(Lw - Nu + Y),$$
$$\partial_j E_{3j} = \varepsilon(Mu - Lv + Z),$$
$$\partial_j E_{4j} = \varepsilon i(Xu + Yv + Zw).$$

These expressions obtained by us in a purely formal way are known to possess physical significance: the first three represent the components of the force exerted by an electromagnetic field on a body of electric charge density ε, and the last (if we neglect the factor i) is the rate at which energy is expended by the field in moving the body. The first three expressions obviously give the right-hand sides of the equations of Euler. Since the left-hand sides also (2.1, 2.2) have been obtained as divergence components (3.6) we may write these equations in an extremely simple form if we introduce a new tensor, which is the difference of the two appearing on the left- and right-hand sides, respectively, viz.,

6.2 $$T_{ij} = M_{ij} - E_{ij}.$$

The equations can then simply be written as

6.3 $$\partial_j T_{ij} = 0 \quad (i = 1, 2, 3).$$

This seems to be very satisfactory, but there is this unpleasant feature about it: the left member of the last equation has a definite meaning not only for the values 1, 2, 3 of i but also for $i = 4$; however, the equations assert something only about the first three values. Let us see what becomes of the left member when the index $i = 4$. The contribution of the tensor M_{ij} seems to give the left member of the continuity equation and is, therefore, zero; but the contribution of the stress-energy tensor E_{ij} is the work performed by the forces on the particle and is, in general, *not zero*. The source of this unpleasantness and the way to remove it will be clear after the reader becomes acquainted with the contents of the next chapter.

It is time now to summarize the present situation. We have eleven fundamental quantities, ρ, u, v, w, p, X, Y, Z, L, M, N. They satisfy certain equations: the Maxwell equations (4.61, 4.62); the equation of continuity (3.5); the equations of motion (6.3). In the last-named equations our eleven quantities enter in certain combinations which are the components of the tensor T_{ij}. For the lack of another name we shall call it the *complete* tensor. This tensor appears then as a very fundamental one. It may be asked whether it determines the eleven quantities which enter into it. If it does, all the quantities we have been considering are, in a general sense, components of one entity, the tensor T_{ij}, and all the equations we have introduced express properties of this tensor. That part of physics which we are discussing in this book, with the exception of the gravitational field, appears then as the study of the tensor T_{ij}. In section 19 we shall prove that T_{ij}, with certain restrictions, determines the quantities ρ, u, v, w, p, X, Y, Z, L, M, N, and in Chapter 5 it will be shown that the gravitational phenomena also are taken care of by it.

2

NEW GEOMETRY

In the preceding chapter we achieved, by introducing an appropriate notation, a great simplicity and uniformity in our formulas. The notation in which indices take the values from 1 to 4 is modeled after that previously introduced in ordinary geometry, the two points of distinction being first that we have four independent variables instead of the three coordinates, and second, that the fourth variable is assigned imaginary values. In spite of these distinctions the analogy with ordinary geometry is very great, and we shall profit very much by pushing this analogy as far as possible and by using geometrical language as well as notation modeled after that of geometry.

One of the purposes of this chapter will be to build a geometry to these specifications: namely, a geometry similar in all respects to ordinary geometry except that it must contain *four* coordinates instead of three and that one of these coordinates must be *imaginary*.

In order to make it easier to grasp the situation we shall discuss the two peculiarities separately: first we will discuss the four-dimensional case with all coordinates real; then we shall consider the three-dimensional case with one coordinate imaginary; and only after that we shall discuss the space we want—the four-dimensional case with one imaginary coordinate.

In this chapter we shall also give a more systematic treatment of tensor analysis than the preliminary sketch of the preceding chapter. This treatment will be divided into two parts: after the sections on four-dimensional geometry with all real coordinates we will introduce tensor analysis corresponding to such a geometry; the modifications made necessary by the imaginary coordinate will be introduced in a special section devoted to that purpose.

7. Analytic geometry of four dimensions

In the present section we shall give a brief outline of properties that we may expect to hold in four-dimensional geometry guided by

26

analogy with two- and three-dimensional geometries; of course, we shall lay stress mainly on those features which we shall need for the application to physics that we have in mind.

To begin with, a point will be represented by four numbers x_1, x_2, x_3, x_4, which we will call the coordinates of the point.

The equations of a straight line we expect to be written in the form

$$7.1 \qquad \frac{x_1 - a_1}{v_1} = \frac{x_2 - a_2}{v_2} = \frac{x_3 - a_3}{v_3} = \frac{x_4 - a_4}{v_4}$$

entirely similar to that used in solid analytic geometry; but we may also use another form. As written the equations state that for every point of the line the four ratios have the same value. Denoting this value by p we may express the condition that a point belongs to the line by writing the coordinates as

$$7.11 \quad x_1 = a_1 + pv_1, \quad x_2 = a_2 + pv_2, \quad x_3 = a_3 + pv_3, \quad x_4 = a_4 + pv_4.$$

As p assumes different values we obtain (for given a_i, v_i) the coordinates of all the different points of the line. The variable p is called the parameter, and this way of describing a line is called "parametric representation." Parametric representation is by no means peculiar to four dimensions; it may be, and is, often used in plane and solid analytic geometry. We present it here because we shall need it later, and it is not always sufficiently emphasized.

A straight line is determined by two points; the equations of the line through the points a_i and b_i is given by the above equations (7.1) in which

$$7.2 \qquad\qquad v_1 = b_1 - a_1, \qquad v_2 = b_2 - a_2, \qquad \text{etc.}$$

Two points determine a directed segment or vector, whose components are the differences between the corresponding coordinates of the points, so that v_i is the component of the vector whose initial point is given by a_i and whose final point is given by b_i.

A vector determined by two points of a straight line is said to belong to that line, and we can use as denominators in the equations 7.1, or as coefficients of p in 7.11, the components of any vector belonging to the straight line.

Two vectors are considered equal if they have equal components; they may, in general, be considered as the opposite sides of a parallelogram. A vector is multiplied by a number by multiplying its components by that number, and two vectors are added by adding their corresponding components.

Two lines are parallel if they contain equal vectors, and it is easy to see that a condition for parallelism of line 7.1 and

7.3
$$\frac{X_1 - A_1}{V_1} = \frac{X_2 - A_2}{V_2} = \frac{X_3 - A_3}{V_3} = \frac{X_4 - A_4}{V_4}$$

is that

$$\frac{v_1}{V_1} = \frac{v_2}{V_2} = \frac{v_3}{V_3} = \frac{v_4}{V_3} \quad \text{or} \quad V_i = av_i,$$

where a is a number, so that proportionality of components of two vectors means parallelism.

Two vectors belonging to two parallel lines (or the same line) are said to have the same direction; two such vectors differ from each other by a numerical factor. It will be convenient to consider the totality of vectors av as constituting a direction so that we can say that two parallel vectors "belong to the same direction."

A condition for *perpendicularity* of these two lines, we expect again by analogy with solid analytic geometry, to be the vanishing of the expression

7.4
$$v_1 V_1 + v_2 V_2 + v_3 V_3 + v_4 V_4,$$

which is called the *inner product* of the two vectors v_i and V_i.

The distance between the points a_1, a_2, a_3, a_4 and b_1, b_2, b_3, b_4 is given by the square root of the expression

7.41 $\quad v_1{}^2 + v_2{}^2 + v_3{}^2 + v_4{}^2 = (a_1 - b_1)^2 + (a_2 - b_2)^2$
$$+ (a_3 - b_3)^2 + (a_4 + b_4)^2.$$

This distance is also considered as the *length* of the vector joining a_i and b_i. The expression for the square of the length of a vector may be considered as a special case of the expression 7.4. We may say, then, that the square of the length of a vector is the square of the vector, i.e., the product of the vector by itself.

We shall use bold-face letters to denote vectors. The inner product of the vectors x and y will be denoted by x · y or xy, and the square of the vector x by x^2.

A vector whose length, or whose square, is unity we shall call a *unit vector*. Its components, we would expect, may be considered as the direction cosines of the line on which the vector lies. We also expect that the inner product of two vectors is equal to the product of their lengths by the cosine of the angle between them.

A *plane* we would expect to be determined by three points not in a line, or by two vectors with the same initial point, or by two lines through a point.   Instead of characterizing a plane by equations we prefer to give it in parametric form; limiting ourselves to a plane through the origin, we have

7.12 $x_1 = pa_1 + qb_1, x_2 = pa_2 + qb_2, x_3 = pa_3 + qb_3, x_4 = pa_4 + qb_4,$

or

$$x_i = pa_i + qb_i,$$

where a_i and b_i are the coordinates of two points in the plane or the components of two vectors of the plane whose initial points may be considered as at the origin.   We shall write this formula also as

7.6 $$\mathbf{x} = \alpha\mathbf{i} + \beta\mathbf{j}$$

where $\mathbf{x}, \mathbf{i}, \mathbf{j}$ stand for vectors whose components are x_i, a_i, b_i and where we use Greek letters for parameters in order to avoid confusion with vectors.   The vectors $\mathbf{i}$ and $\mathbf{j}$ must not, of course, have the same direction or, as we shall say, they must be independent.

Every pair of coordinate axes determines a plane, and since six pairs can be formed from four objects we have six coordinate planes.

In the same way that the direction of a straight line is determined by a configuration of two points on it, that is, a vector, the "orientation" of a plane may be determined by the configuration of three points on it, that is, a triangle.   A vector is given by its components, which are the lengths of its projections on the coordinate axes.   In the same way a triangle may be characterized (to a certain extent) by the areas of its projections on the coordinate *planes*.   If, for example, we take a triangle one of whose vertices is at the origin 0, 0, 0, 0, and the two others at the points x_i and y_i respectively, the areas of the projections will be the quantities

$$A_{ij} = \frac{1}{2}\begin{vmatrix} x_i & x_j \\ y_i & y_j \end{vmatrix},$$

which satisfy the relation

$$A_{ij} + A_{ji} = 0.$$

The six numbers A_{12}, A_{13}, A_{23}, A_{14}, A_{24}, and A_{34} are considered the components of a new kind of magnitude (sometimes called a six-vector).   For the three-dimensional space we could introduce quantities A_{ij} in an analogous way, but the numbers A_{12}, A_{13}, A_{23} would not have the same importance as the A_{ij} have in four-space because in three-space they may be considered as the components of an ordinary vector perpendicular to the plane of the triangle.   This is not true of the six quantities A_{ij} in four-space, for there the vectors per-

plane of a triangle do not all have the same direction,
each of them has only four components.

ting that this peculiarity of four-dimensional space as
three-dimensional, viz., the appearance of a new kind of
finds a counterpart in physics. In fact, there we intro-
nsor with (essentially) six components F_{ij} (compare 4.4),
three which were identified with the electric, and the other three
with the magnetic, force components. It appears that ten of our
fundamental quantities ρu, ρv, ρw, ρ, X, Y, Z, L, M, N, therefore,
permit a geometrical interpretation; the first four are considered as
the four projections of a part of a straight line on the coordinate axes,
the remaining six as the projections of a part of a plane on the coordinate planes.

A little against our expectations, however, these six quantities A_{ij}
are not independent, for, as the reader will easily verify,

7.7 $$A_{12} \cdot A_{34} + A_{31} \cdot A_{24} + A_{23} \cdot A_{14} = 0.$$

We have here a relation that exists in the mathematical theory. At
once the question arises: Does a corresponding relation hold for the
corresponding quantities in the physical theory? According to
formulas 4.5 this would mean

$$L \cdot X + M \cdot Y + N \cdot Z = 0,$$

i.e., perpendicularity of the electric and magnetic force vectors.
These vectors are, however, known not to be necessarily perpendicular
to each other, so that our identification must be faulty. A slight
modification helps to overcome the difficulty, for, if instead of considering the areas of projections of a triangular contour, we consider
the areas of projections of an arbitrary contour, which is not necessarily flat, then the six quantities are independent and the formal
analogy holds perfectly.

Returning to the plane, we mention that, although it might seem
strange at first glance, it can happen that two planes have only one
point in common, a situation that never occurs in three dimensions.
An example of two planes with only one common point is given by the
$x_1 x_2$ and the $x_3 x_4$ coordinate planes where the common point is, of
course, the origin.

Four points not in a plane, or three vectors with a common origin,
we expect to determine a "solid" which may be defined as the totality
of points of three kinds: (1) points on the lines determined by the
given vectors; (2) points on lines joining two points of the first kind;
and (3) points of lines joining two points of the second kind. In

ordinary geometry a configuration defined in this way exhausts all points, but this not so in our four-dimensional geometry. As examples we have the four coordinate solids, which are the totalities of points satisfying the relations $x_1 = 0$, $x_2 = 0$, $x_3 = 0$, $x_4 = 0$, respectively.

A parametric representation of a solid is analogous to that of a plane. For a solid through the origin we have as such parametric representation

7.61 $$\mathbf{x} = \alpha\mathbf{i} + \beta\mathbf{j} + \gamma\mathbf{k};$$

where $\mathbf{i}, \mathbf{j}, \mathbf{k}$ are three vectors that do not lie in the same plane.

For all possible values of α, β, γ we obtain all the points of the solid through the origin which is determined by the vectors $\mathbf{i}, \mathbf{j}, \mathbf{k}$.

Next we consider a configuration determined by five points not in a solid; we obtain all the points of our four-dimensional space. Incidentally, as a generalization of the formulas 7.6 and 7.61, we now have

7.62 $$\mathbf{x} = \alpha\mathbf{i} + \beta\mathbf{j} + \gamma\mathbf{k} + \delta\mathbf{l}.$$

This formula gives the expression of every vector with initial point at the origin in terms of four vectors not all in the same solid.   Expressions similar to 7.6, 7.61, 7.62, i.e., sums of products of vectors multiplied by numbers, we shall call linear combinations of vectors, and the numerical factors we shall call the coefficients of the linear combinations.   We can say then that any vector in the plane, or a solid, or a four-space, can be written as a linear combination of two, or three, or four independent vectors; by independent vectors we mean two vectors not of the same direction, or three vectors not in the same plane, etc.   The general definition will be given later.

We started this section with the assumption that there exists such a thing as four-dimensional space and that its points can be represented by quadruples of numbers.   In trying to build an analytic geometry on that basis we are essentially in the position of a student who attempts to study solid *analytic* geometry without any knowledge of solid geometry and without any space intuition.   Of course, we have analogy with three-dimensional space to guide us, but analogy can misguide as well as guide.   As a matter of fact our position is worse, because if we want to associate the fourth coordinate with time our *intuition* seems to say very clearly that time has entirely different properties from space.   Still our *formulas* and the analogy with three-space strongly suggest that x_1, x_2, x_3, and $x_4 = ti$ can and should be treated on the same footing.   Thus we have a conflict between our intuition and our formulas, and if we want to find out what lies behind the unmistakable regularities manifested in the formulas of Chapter 1 we must temporarily lay our intuition aside and be guided by formal considerations.

We will achieve our purpose in two steps: first we will free ourselves of the exclusive dominance of one fixed representation (which we expect in analogy to three dimensions to be interpretable as the result of using a particular system of reference); and then, in the next section, we will show that it is possible to build the whole structure without assuming any a priori system of reference—in fact, to build it in Euclidean fashion on an axiomatic or, using a more modern term, on a postulational basis.

8. Transformation of coordinates

In plane and solid analytic geometry the concept of transformation of coordinates plays an important part both from the practical and from the theoretical point of view. From the practical point of view the possibility of changing the coordinate system permits the reference system to be adapted to the particular properties of the object of study (for instance, using the principal axes of an ellipse as coordinate axes reduces the equation to a very simple standard form) or to the convenience of the observer (as when we direct the x axis toward us, the y axis to our right, and so on). An even more important aspect is the theoretical one.

In order to bring out this importance let us consider a case when such a transformation is not applicable. Let us compare *plane geometry* with a *two-way diagram*. Both in plane geometry and in a diagram we use coordinate axes, but in geometry the axes play an auxiliary role, since we express, by referring to axes, properties of configurations which exist and could be treated without any axes. Moreover, if we use a set of axes we could use any other just as well (except for practical considerations). The situation is different when we use a plane as a means of representing a functional dependence between two quantities of different kind, that is, when we have a diagram. We may, for instance, use the two axes to plot temperature against pressure, or the height of an individual against the number of individuals of that height in a certain population. In the majority of such cases the axes play an essential part in the discussion, for if we delete the axes the diagram loses its meaning. Also rotation of axes has no sense. (In describing the motion of a point along a line we also can use a diagram, plotting time along one axis and the position of the point on the other. Such a diagram has a direct bearing on the main topic of our discussion—in it we essentially consider time as one of the coordinates much in the same way as in Chapter 1. In a sense, four-dimensional space may be considered as an [abstract] diagram. Is it *just* a diagram, or something more, something like a geometry? It is for the discussion of this question that we must prepare ourselves in this chapter. Now since the difference reduces to the question of whether transformation of coordinates has a meaning in this case, it is important for us to discuss, in full, the general question of transformation of coordinates.)

In analytic geometry we usually consider translation and rotation of axes. The first does not present any difficulties, since even if we do not consider time as a coordinate we can change t by counting time from a different moment, and that means the addition of a constant, i.e., a transformation $t = t' + t_0$ analogous to translation of axes. Moreover, a transformation of this type does not change vectors, nor does it change derivatives with respect to coordinates. We may, therefore, speaking of transformation of coordinates, limit ourselves to what corresponds to *rotation* of axes. This is the reason why we shall speak of transformations of components of vectors rather than of transformations of coordinates of points in what follows.

We saw that any vector in the plane may be represented as a linear combination of two fixed (non-collinear) vectors and that these fixed vectors can be chosen arbitrarily. Similarly, in the case of a solid we may use three fixed but arbitrarily chosen vectors (not in the same plane) to represent any vector in the solid, and finally, we may use any *four* independent vectors to represent any vector in four-space. If, in particular, we choose as such the four vectors $\mathbf{i} = (1, 0, 0, 0)$, $\mathbf{j} = (0, 1, 0, 0)$, $\mathbf{k} = (0, 0, 1, 0)$, and $\mathbf{l} = (0, 0, 0, 1)$ a vector of components u_1, u_2, u_3, u_4 will be represented by

$$u_1\mathbf{i} + u_2\mathbf{j} + u_3\mathbf{k} + u_4\mathbf{l}.$$

For this particular choice of fixed vectors the coefficients in the linear combination representing a vector are the same numbers as those by which the vector was originally given. A similar representation can be used with any four fixed independent vectors, and we have therefore succeeded in presenting the components u_1, u_2, u_3, u_4 as a special case of a more general way of representing a vector. The originally given numbers have then lost their preferential status since we can introduce (using these numbers, of course) some other four independent vectors $\mathbf{i}', \mathbf{j}', \mathbf{k}', \mathbf{l}'$ and the four numbers which will appear as the coefficients in the linear combination representing $\mathbf{u}$ in the form

$$u_1'\mathbf{i}' + u_2'\mathbf{j}' + u_3'\mathbf{k}' + u_4'\mathbf{l}'$$

will be as good as the original numbers u_1, u_2, u_3, u_4. This may seem trivial to the reader, but it should be remembered that we are laying the foundations for freeing ourselves of the domination of absolute time, which is equivalent to a freedom of choice for l' as well as i', j', k'.

It is of secondary importance that we impose certain conditions on the choice of the reference vectors for convenience. In the plane we may choose two mutually perpendicular unit vectors. This restriction is expressed in the formulas

8.1 $$i^2 = 1, \qquad j^2 = 1, \qquad ij = 0.$$

For a solid we may consider three mutually perpendicular unit vectors. This restriction is expressed by adding

8.11 $$k^2 = 1, \qquad ki = 0, \qquad kj = 0,$$

to the above formulas 8.1. Similarly, for the whole space, we may add the relations

8.12 $$l^2 = 1, \qquad li = 0, \qquad lj = 0, \qquad lk = 0.$$

A set satisfying these restrictions, that is a set of mutually perpendicular unit vectors (two or three or four, as the case may be), is called an *orthonormal* set.

In this chapter and the next we will assume that this restriction is imposed, but it is not necessary and we will see later that in some situations it is no longer convenient.

As far as applications to the theory of relativity are concerned we will not need to go beyond four dimensions (although five-dimensional and even six-dimensional geometry has been used on occasions to interpret physical phenomena). However, if we use, as we intend to do, the simplifying notations introduced in section 3, the number of dimensions does not show up in the formulas. If we write e_1 for i, e_2 for j, e_3 for k, and e_4 for l and u_1 for α, u_2 for β, u_3 for γ, and u_4 for δ, then formulas 7.6, 7.61, and 7.62 can be all written in one form, namely,

8.2 $$u = u_i e_i,$$

where the summation is extended from 1 to 2, to 3, or to 4 as the case may be. If we deal with a space of a definite number of dimensions the summations in all discussions are assumed to be extended accordingly. Since many discussions apply equally well to any number of dimensions it is often unnecessary to pay much attention to this. In fact, only when spaces of different numbers of dimensions occur in the same discussion does it become necessary to use the summation sign Σ and to indicate explicitly the range of the indices (compare section 21).

Formulas 8.1, which express the fact that the vectors are orthonormal, may be written in index notations as

8.3 $$\mathbf{e}_i \mathbf{e}_j = \delta_{ij},$$

where δ_{ij} is the symbol defined in section 3 (after formulas 3.4).

If we want to pass from an orthonormal set $\mathbf{e}_i$ to another orthonormal set $\mathbf{e}_i'$ we observe that since every vector $\mathbf{e}_i$ is a linear combination of the vectors $\mathbf{e}_i'$ we can write

8.4 $$\mathbf{e}_i = a_{ij}\mathbf{e}_j',$$

and if a vector $\mathbf{u}$ has components u_i with respect to the set $\mathbf{e}_i$ so that

8.5 $$\mathbf{u} = u_i\mathbf{e}_i,$$

its components with respect to the $\mathbf{e}_j'$ may be obtained by substituting 8.4 into 8.5. We have then

$$\mathbf{u} = u_i a_{ij}\mathbf{e}_j',$$

so that the components of $\mathbf{u}$ with respect to the $\mathbf{e}_j'$, which we denote by u_j', are seen to be

8.6 $$u_j' = u_i a_{ij}.$$

The coefficients a_{ij} are n^2 in number, but they are not independent. If we want to find the restrictions to which they are subjected we should use the fact that both systems $\mathbf{e}_i$ and $\mathbf{e}_j'$ are orthonormal, that is, satisfy relations 8.3. We therefore obtain

$$\mathbf{e}_i \cdot \mathbf{e}_k = a_{ij}\mathbf{e}_j' \cdot a_{ks}\mathbf{e}_{ks}' = a_{ij}a_{ks}\mathbf{e}_j'\mathbf{e}_s'$$

or

8.7 $$\delta_{ik} = a_{ij}a_{ks}\delta_{js} = a_{ij}a_{kj}.$$

Exercise 1. Prove that the coefficients a_{ij} are the direction cosines of the vectors of one system with respect to the other.

Exercise 2. Compare for the case $n = 3$ the formulas 8.6 and 8.7 with the formulas for rotation of axes used in solid analytic geometry.

As in solid geometry it is always possible to achieve a general rotation of axes by successive rotations in coordinates planes instead of by using formulas 8.6. In other words, it is possible to replace the vectors $\mathbf{i}, \mathbf{j}, \mathbf{k}, \mathbf{l}$ by the vectors $\mathbf{i}', \mathbf{j}', \mathbf{k}', \mathbf{l}'$ in successive steps, each of which involves the replacement of one pair by another pair in the same plane. Of course, we can write

$$\mathbf{e_1}' = a_{11}\mathbf{e_1} + a_{12}\mathbf{e_2}, \qquad \mathbf{e_2}' = a_{21}\mathbf{e_1} + a_{22}\mathbf{e_2},$$

where the a's are subjected to relations 8.7, but it is easy to see that then

8.8 $a_{11} = \cos\theta, \quad a_{12} = -\sin\theta, \quad a_{21} = \pm\sin\theta, \quad a_{22} = \pm\cos\theta,$

where θ is the angle of rotation and the double signs may be omitted if we are interested only in the directions of the vectors or the coordinate axes and not in their sense. The upper signs correspond to pure rotation and the lower signs to rotation combined with reflection.

9. Postulates for four-dimensional geometry

Until now we have been listing some propositions which "we might expect in four-dimensional geometry if there were such a thing." One may expect here a question: *Is* there such a thing? Some people are not troubled by questions of this kind and are willing to accept four-dimensional geometry without further discussion. If the reader feels that way he may omit this section. For the others we will attempt to remove all possible doubt by presenting a rigorous exposition.

According to the point of view we have adopted, geometry has two aspects: on the one hand it has a logical structure in that it consists of propositions some of which are postulated (or adopted as definitions) and the rest derived from them logically; on the other hand there is a question of applicability in that some of these propositions are applied to the "outside world" as a result of identification of certain terms of the theory with certain features of our experience. Consequently the question of "existence" ("is there such a thing?") does not seem proper. It is more appropriate to inquire into the questions of consistency of the theory and its applicability, or the success of its application. This section will be devoted to the first question.

However, this question will not be discussed in detail. We shall limit ourselves to giving a list of postulates on which geometry can be based and a few indications as to how a complete theory can be developed from these postulates.

As our fundamental undefined concept we choose "vector" and "point" and we will consider real numbers as given. The fundamental operations will be "addition of vectors," "multiplication of a vector by a number," "inner multiplication of vectors," and "subtraction of points." The properties of these operations are listed below.

POSTULATE I.   Every two vectors have a sum.   Addition is commutative, i.e., $a + b = b + a$, and associative, i.e., $a + (b + c) =$ $(a + b) + c$; subtraction is unique; i.e., for every two vectors a and b there exists one and only one vector x such that $a = b + x$.   It follows that there exists a vector 0 that satisfies the relation $a + 0 =$ a for every a.

POSTULATE II.   Given a number α and a vector a there exists a vector αa or $a\alpha$ which is called their product.   The associative law holds in the sense that $\alpha(\beta a) = (\alpha\beta)a$.   Similarly the distributive laws $(\alpha + \beta)a = \alpha a + \beta a$ and $\alpha(a + b) = \alpha a + \alpha b$ are valid.

Before we formulate the next postulate we introduce the following

DEFINITION.   The vectors $a, b, c \cdots$ are called (linearly) dependent if there exist numbers $\alpha, \beta, \gamma \cdots$, not all zero, such that

$$\alpha a + \beta b + \gamma c + \cdots = 0.$$

They are called independent when no such numbers exist.

POSTULATE III.   There are four independent vectors; every five vectors are dependent.

POSTULATE IV.   To every two vectors a and b corresponds a number $a \cdot b$ or ab called their (inner) product.   Inner multiplication is commutative: $a \cdot b = b \cdot a$.   It obeys together with multiplication of vectors by numbers the associative law, $\alpha(a \cdot b) = (\alpha a \cdot b)$; and, together with addition, the distributive law $a \cdot (b + c) = a \cdot b + a \cdot c$.

POSTULATE V.   If a vector is not zero its square is positive.

If we want to have a geometry we must add to these postulates on vectors some statements concerning points, and as such we may take:

POSTULATE VI.   Every two points A, B have as their difference a vector, h; or in formulas $B - A = h$, $B = A + h$.

POSTULATE VII. $(A - B) + (B - C) = A - C$.

The body of propositions which may be deduced from these postulates we shall call four-dimensional geometry.

To prove that the whole of geometry can be deduced from propositions I–VII we would have to actually deduce it.   We shall not do this, of course, but we shall indicate how analytic geometry can be arrived at in the following discussion, which is meant to be entirely formal; i.e., it is not intended to invoke our intuition but only the properties stated in the postulates.

By length of a vector we mean the positive square root of the product of the vector by itself: $|a| = \sqrt{a^2}$.   Two vectors are considered perpendicular if their inner product is zero.   A vector is called a unit vector if its length is equal to 1.

The angle between two vectors is defined by the formula

$$\cos \phi = \frac{\mathbf{x} \cdot \mathbf{y}}{|\mathbf{x}| \cdot |\mathbf{y}|}.$$

We must prove, of course, that this formula defines a real angle (uniquely, if we limit it to belong to the first and second quadrants). For this purpose it is enough to prove that the absolute value of the right member does not exceed unity, or that

$$(\mathbf{x} \cdot \mathbf{y})^2 - \mathbf{x}^2 \mathbf{y}^2 \geq 0.$$

If we form the linear combination $\mathbf{v} = \lambda\mathbf{x} + \mu\mathbf{y}$ its square is

$$\lambda^2 \mathbf{x}^2 + 2\lambda\mu\mathbf{x} \cdot \mathbf{y} + \mu^2 \mathbf{y}^2.$$

Now the above inequality, which expresses the fact that the discriminant of this expression is negative or zero, is seen to be a consequence of the fact that $\mathbf{v}^2 \geq 0$, a consequence of postulate V.

A set of mutually perpendicular unit vectors is called an *orthonormal* set.

THEOREM. There exists an orthonormal set of four vectors, and every vector can be expressed as a linear combination of them.

Proof. First, given any vector $\mathbf{a}$ we can divide it by the square root of its square and the resulting vector will be a unit vector. Such a vector may be considered as forming an orthonormal set of one vector. Denote by r the greatest number of vectors in an orthonormal set, and call the vectors of such a set of r vectors $\mathbf{i}, \mathbf{j}, \mathbf{k}$, etc. Then, for any vector $\mathbf{x}$, form the vector

$$\mathbf{y} = \mathbf{x} - \mathbf{i}(\mathbf{ix}) - \mathbf{j}(\mathbf{jx}) - \text{etc.}$$

Multiplying by $\mathbf{i}$ we get

$$\mathbf{yi} = \mathbf{ix} - \mathbf{i}^2(\mathbf{ix}) - \mathbf{ij}(\mathbf{jx}) - \text{etc;}$$

using the relations 8.1, etc., which express orthonormality we find that $\mathbf{yi} = \mathbf{0}$, and in the same way we find that $\mathbf{yj} = \mathbf{0}$, $\mathbf{yk} = \mathbf{0}$, etc., i.e., that $\mathbf{y}$ is perpendicular to all the vectors of the set. Now, if $\mathbf{y}$ were not zero, $|\mathbf{y}|$, by postulate V, is also not zero and $\mathbf{y}/|\mathbf{y}|$ is a unit vector. It, together with the given vectors, would constitute an orthonormal set of $r + 1$ vectors, which contradicts the assumption that r was the largest number of vectors in an orthonormal set. Therefore, $\mathbf{y} = \mathbf{0}$ and we have

9.1 $$\mathbf{x} = \mathbf{i}(\mathbf{ix}) + \mathbf{j}(\mathbf{jx}) + \cdots$$

for every vector **x**.   If there were fewer than four vectors in the set
we are considering, then any four vectors would be dependent, contrary to postulate III.

The vectors of an orthonormal set we shall call coordinate vectors.
We shall call the quantities $x_1 = \mathbf{ix}$, $x_2 = \mathbf{jx}$, $x_3 = \mathbf{kx}$, $x_4 = \mathbf{lx}$ the
components of **x** with respect to **i, j, k, l**.   A point O together with a
set of coordinate vectors we shall call a coordinate system.   Given
a coordinate system we can assign to every point X four coordinates
in the following way: denote the vector $X - O$ by **x** (according to
postulate VI); and call the components of the vector **x** the *coordinates*
of the point X.   If now we choose another origin O' and the same set of
coordinate vectors, the coordinates of the point X will be the components of $X - O'$.   Since, according to postulate VII, $X - O =$
$(X - O') + (O' - O)$, the old coordinates will be equal to the new
coordinates plus the old coordinates of the new origin.   A connection
is thus established with ordinary analytic geometry.

Formula 9.1 may be compared with formula 7.62.   It may also be
written as

9.2 $$\mathbf{x} = x_1\mathbf{i} + x_2\mathbf{j} + x_3\mathbf{k} + x_4\mathbf{l}.$$

10. Tensor analysis

We wish to substitute now a more satisfactory definition for the
preliminary definitions of tensor analysis suggested by the formal
development in Chapter 1.   At that time we considered symbols with
two (or more) indices as tensor components in analogy to symbols
with one index which stand for vector components,   But we *know*
what a vector is, and the use of components of a vector is just a method
of representing that known thing.   In the case of tensors we seem to
have to take representation as the starting point of our study.   The
situation seems complicated since the fact that there is not one but
many different representations of the same vector (depending on the
coordinate system we use) leads us to think that the same general
situation will obtain for tensors, and the question arises, naturally,
how we shall be able to find out, given two representations of a tensor,
whether it is the same tensor that is represented in the two cases;
or, given a representation of a tensor in one system of coordinates,
how the representation of *the same tensor* in a given other system can
be obtained.   In order to be able to answer such questions intelli-
gently we want to introduce the idea of the tensor itself and to consider
the components as something secondary.   In the beginning we shall
limit ourselves to the consideration of two dimensions.

We look then for some entity of which the components will be the constituent parts. The first thing that occurs to our mind in connection with the components a_{11}, a_{12}, a_{21}, a_{22} is the determinant

$$\Delta = \begin{vmatrix} a_{11} & a_{12} \\ a_{21} & a_{22} \end{vmatrix},$$

but, although the value of Δ is determined by the values a_{ij}, it is not true that Δ in turn determines the components a_{ij}.

Another example of two index symbols occurring in mathematics is found in quadratic forms. We may write the equation of a central conic, for example, $ax^2 + 2bxy + cy^2 = 1$, by introducing the notations x_1 for x, x_2 for y, a_{11} for a, a_{12} and a_{21} for b, and a_{22} for c, in the form

$$a_{11}x_1x_1 + a_{12}x_1x_2 + a_{21}x_2x_1 + a_{22}x_2x_2 = 1.$$

Let us consider the left-hand side of this equation. Here the components a_{ij} are combined (together with the variables x_1, x_2) into one expression, and they can, to a certain extent, be gotten back from that expression. If we set $x_1 = 1$, $x_2 = 0$, for instance, we obtain a_{11} as the value of the expression. The component a_{22} can be obtained in a similar way, but it would be difficult to imagine how a_{12} could be obtained; in fact, it is impossible to get a_{12} from this expression, because two expressions which differ in the values of a_{12} and a_{21} but for which $a_{12} + a_{21}$ has the same value would give the same results for all combinations of x_1, x_2. A slight generalization will, however, obviate this difficulty. This generalization is suggested by the equation of the tangent (or polar) to the above conic, which can be written as

$$a_{11}x_1y_1 + a_{12}x_1y_2 + a_{21}x_2y_1 + a_{22}x_2y_2 = 1.$$

If we substitute into the left-hand side of this equation $x_1 = 1$, $x_2 = 0$, $y_1 = 0$, $y_2 = 1$ we obtain a_{12}. We can say therefore about the bilinear form

10.1 $\phi = a_{11}x_1y_1 + a_{12}x_1y_2 + a_{21}x_2y_1 + a_{22}x_2y_2$

not only that it is determined by the components a_{ij} but also that it permits us to determine these components. It appears therefore that we can use it in defining a tensor.

In the case of vectors, although they may be given by components, we can say what a vector is without referring to a coordinate system. We would like to achieve the same situation in the case of tensors. The consideration of the bilinear form will permit us to do that.

First, we observe that we may free ourselves of the dependence on the *particular system* of coordinates we are using. The variables x_1, x_2 and y_1, y_2 may be considered as the components of two vectors, and the above expression 10.1 furnishes us then a numerical value every time these two vectors are given. It may be considered as defining a function ϕ, the arguments of which are the two vectors and whose values are the numbers calculated by substituting the components of these vectors in the expression 10.1. This functional dependence we may consider *as the tensor*. If we want to use another coordinate system we shall have the same vectors given by different components x_1', x_2' and y_1', y_2' and we expect to find another expression of the same type as 10.1 involving these new components, say

$$10.11 \qquad \phi = a_{11}'x_1'y_1' + a_{12}'x_1'y_2' + a_{21}'x_2'y_1' + a_{22}'x_2'y_2',$$

which would assign the same values to the two vectors. The coefficients will, of course, be different, and these new coefficients we shall consider as the *new components* of the *same tensor* in the *new* coordinate system.

Let us perform the calculation. If we rotate our axes through an angle θ the old coordinates are expressed in the new coordinates by the formulas

$$10.2 \qquad\qquad x_1 = x_1'c - x_2's, \qquad x_2 = x_1's + x_2'c,$$

where

$$10.3 \qquad\qquad c = \cos\theta, \qquad s = \sin\theta.$$

The components of the other vector y_1, y_2 will be expressed by analogous formulas in terms of the new components of the same vector. Substituting these expressions in the above bilinear form (10.1) we obtain

$$a_{11}(x_1'c - x_2's)(y_1'c - y_2's) + a_{12}(x_1'c - x_2's)(y_1's + y_2'c)$$
$$+ a_{21}(x_1's + x_2'c)(y_1'c - y_2's) + a_{22}(x_1's + x_2'c)(y_1's + y_2'c),$$

which may be written as 10.11 if we give to a_{ij}' the values

$$10.21 \qquad
\begin{aligned}
a_{11}' &= a_{11}c^2 + a_{12}cs + a_{21}sc + a_{22}s^2, \\
a_{12}' &= -a_{11}cs + a_{12}c^2 - a_{21}s^2 + a_{22}sc, \\
a_{21}' &= -a_{11}sc - a_{12}s^2 + a_{21}c^2 + a_{22}cs, \\
a_{22}' &= a_{11}s^2 - a_{12}sc - a_{21}cs + a_{22}c^2.
\end{aligned}$$

These are the new components of the tensor whose old components are the a_{ij}. The equation of the conic section in the new coordinates has the same form as in the old system. We may say that formula 10.11 expresses the same functional dependence on the two vectors using their new components as 10.1 does using their old components.

Exercise 1. Find which of the following relations or sets of relations are not affected by the transformations 10.21:

(a) $a_{12} = a_{21}$; (b) $a_{12} + a_{21} = 0$; (c) $a_{12} + a_{21} = 0$, $a_{11} = 0$, $a_{22} = 0$;

(d) $a_{11} = a_{22}$.

The components of a tensor *change*, in general, when we pass from one coordinate system to another, but there are certain combinations that do not change; for example, if we add together the first and the last of the four above equalities we obtain, taking into account that

10.4 $$c^2 + s^2 = 1,$$

the relation

10.5 $$a_{11}' + a_{22}' = a_{11} + a_{22}.$$

Exercise 2. Prove that the determinant

10.51 $$\begin{vmatrix} a_{11} & a_{12} \\ a_{21} & a_{22} \end{vmatrix}.$$

is not affected by the substitution of the primed components for the unprimed ones.

Expressions of this kind are called invariants.

As was mentioned in section 8, the freedom we have in choosing a coordinate system (or the freedom to change from one coordinate system to another) can be used to simplify expressions. For instance, if in the above tensor $a_{12} = a_{21}$ the same relation will hold in the transformed tensor, i.e., we will have $a_{12}' = a_{21}'$, and in this case we can choose the angle θ so as to make this last quantity zero; such a value of θ can be found by making

$$\tan 2\theta = \frac{2a_{12}}{a_{11} - a_{22}}.$$

This corresponds to transformation to principal axes in the equation of a central conic.

Returning to the general discussion of a tensor we can now go a step further and not only free ourselves of the dependence on a particular system of coordinates but also dispense with the use of coordinates altogether. We said that we shall consider as a tensor a function (given by the expression 10.1) of two vectors. The statement that a tensor is a numerically valued function of two vectors does not involve coordinates, but the special type of functional dependence is given by a formula (namely, 10.1) which makes use of coordinates. However, it is possible to characterize this type of dependence without using them, as we shall see in what follows.

We say, in general, that $\phi(\mathbf{x})$ depends on its argument $\mathbf{x}$ linearly if

10.6 $$\phi(\lambda\mathbf{x} + \mu\mathbf{y}) = \lambda\phi(\mathbf{x}) + \mu\phi(\mathbf{y}).$$

It is easy to see that linearity defined in terms of coordinates as dependence involving only first powers of the components satisfies this condition. We arrive thus at the following definition of a tensor:

A tensor of rank r is a function which assigns to r vector arguments numerical values, the dependence on each argument being linear in the sense of 10.6.

Exercise 3. Prove that the inner product of two vectors is a tensor of rank two.

Exercise 4. Prove that the inner product of a *constant* vector $\mathbf{v}$ and a variable vector $\mathbf{x}$ is a tensor of rank one.

Exercise 5. We can mention here another example of a tensor which was not complicated enough to introduce the concept but which can serve as an illustration of it. If we write the equation of a straight line in the plane as $ax + by = c$ we can rewrite it using index notation as

$$a_1x_1 + a_2x_2 = c.$$

The left member is a tensor of rank one. Find how the coefficients a_1 and a_2 change when we pass to another system of coordinates.

We can prove that an expression of a tensor as a bilinear (or multilinear) form may be gotten back from this general definition. In fact, if given, for example, a tensor of rank two, with two vector arguments $\phi(\mathbf{x}, \mathbf{y})$, we substitute for $\mathbf{x}$ and $\mathbf{y}$ their expressions in terms of components and unit vectors (see 7.6),

$$\mathbf{x} = \mathbf{i}x_1 + \mathbf{j}x_2, \qquad \mathbf{y} = \mathbf{i}y_1 + \mathbf{j}y_2,$$

we may write, using the above definition of a tensor and that of linearity (10.6):

10.61 $\quad\phi(\mathbf{x}, \mathbf{y}) = \phi(\mathbf{i}x_1 + \mathbf{j}x_2, \mathbf{i}y_1 + \mathbf{j}y_2)$

$$= \phi(\mathbf{i}, \mathbf{i})x_1y_1 + \phi(\mathbf{i}, \mathbf{j})x_1y_2 + \phi(\mathbf{j}, \mathbf{i})x_2y_1 + \phi(\mathbf{j}, \mathbf{j})x_2y_2.$$

We see that this expression differs from that given by 10.1 as a bilinear form only in that $\phi(\mathbf{i}, \mathbf{i})$, $\phi(\mathbf{i}, \mathbf{j})$, $\phi(\mathbf{j}, \mathbf{i})$, $\phi(\mathbf{j}, \mathbf{j})$ appear instead of a_{11}, a_{12}, a_{21}, and a_{22}. From this point of view the *concept* of a tensor is entirely independent of a coordinate system and of components. We obtain tensor *components* when we introduce a set of coordinate vectors, and transformation of coordinates corresponds to replacing of one set of coordinate vectors by a new set.

The concept of a tensor and the above definition do not depend at all on the number of dimensions of the space. When it comes to coordinate representation, we have to use, of course, in a space of n dimensions n coordinate vectors, but with our notation the formulas still will be independent of the number of dimensions. The definition of linear dependence will be the same as that given above by formula 10.6. It is easily generalized to any number of vectors. We can write, if ϕ is a linear function,

$$\phi(\lambda \mathbf{x} + \mu \mathbf{y} + \nu \mathbf{z} + \cdots) = \lambda \phi(\mathbf{x}) + \mu \phi(\mathbf{y}) + \nu \phi(\mathbf{z}) + \cdots$$

and say in words that the result of the application of a linear function ϕ to a linear combination of vectors is a linear combination with the same coefficients of the results of the application of ϕ to these vectors. If we denote by $\mathbf{e}_i$ a fixed set of n independent vectors, any vector $\mathbf{x}$, as we know, can be written as $\mathbf{x} = x_i \mathbf{e}_i$. If $\phi(\mathbf{x})$ is a tensor of rank one we substitute that expression and obtain, using linearity, $\phi(\mathbf{x}) = \phi(\mathbf{e}_i x_i) = x_i \phi(\mathbf{e}_i)$; we shall call the numbers $\phi(\mathbf{e}_i)$ the components of the tensor $\phi(\mathbf{x})$, and we will write ϕ_i for $\phi(\mathbf{e}_i)$.

For a tensor of rank two we will have

$$\phi(\mathbf{x}, \mathbf{y}) = \phi(x_i \mathbf{e}_i, y_j \mathbf{e}_j)$$

(we have to be careful to avoid writing $y_i \mathbf{e}_i$ for $\mathbf{y}$ in the same formula in which we have $x_i \mathbf{e}_i$ because it would lead to confusion since we agreed to sum wherever an index appears twice). Using linearity we further have

$$\phi(\mathbf{x}, \mathbf{y}) = x_i y_j \phi(\mathbf{e}_i, \mathbf{e}_j).$$

The components $\phi(e_i, e_j)$ will be denoted by ϕ_{ij}.

In section 3 we introduced the Kronecker symbols δ_{ij}. Can we consider these as the components of a tensor in some coordinate system? If we can, the value of this tensor will be given by the expression $\delta_{ij} x_i y_j$, and this is easily seen (using the definition of δ_{ij}) to be equal to $x_i y_i$, that is, the inner product of the vectors $\mathbf{x}$ and $\mathbf{y}$. This is true no matter what coordinate system we are using as long as it is rectangular. We may speak then of the tensor of components δ_{ij} without specifying the coordinate system (in the case of other tensors, as we know, the components change when we pass to another coordinate system).

In section 4 we introduced the notation F_{ij} for the components of the electric and magnetic forces and we considered them as the components of a tensor of rank two. Is this justified from the point of view we have adopted now? If we try to set up a quadratic form $F_{ij}u_iu_j$ we discover that because of the relations $F_{ij} + F_{ji} = 0$ this form is identically zero. However, we can write the *bilinear* form $F_{ij}u_iv_j$, where u_i and v_j are the components of two variable vectors **u** and **v**, and this expression represents, according to our definition, a tensor of rank two which we may denote by $F(\mathbf{u}, \mathbf{v})$. If, forgetting for the present the imaginary character of the fourth coordinate, we introduce as coordinate vectors the vectors $\mathbf{i} = (1, 0, 0, 0)$, $\mathbf{j} = (0, 1, 0, 0)$, $\mathbf{k} = (0, 0, 1, 0)$, $\mathbf{l} = (0, 0, 0, 1)$, we can write

$$\mathbf{u} = u_1\mathbf{i} + u_2\mathbf{j} + u_3\mathbf{k} + u_4\mathbf{l}; \quad \mathbf{v} = v_1\mathbf{i} + v_2\mathbf{j} + v_3\mathbf{k} + v_4\mathbf{l}.$$

Substituting this into $F(\mathbf{u}, \mathbf{v})$, we find that F_{ij} are the components of the tensor $F(\mathbf{u}, \mathbf{v})$. The relations $F_{ij} + F_{ji} = 0$ to which the components are subjected can be easily shown to result in the relation

10.62 $$F(\mathbf{u}, \mathbf{v}) = -F(\mathbf{v}, \mathbf{u}),$$

which gives a property called antisymmetry, or skew-symmetry, of the tensor expressed independently of components.

Now if we want to find the components of $F(\mathbf{u}, \mathbf{v})$ in any other coordinate system we must use instead of **i**, **j**, **k**, **l** the unit vectors $\mathbf{i'}$, $\mathbf{j'}$, $\mathbf{k'}$, $\mathbf{l'}$ of that other system; denoting these components by F_{ij}', we have, for instance,

$$F_{12}' = F(\mathbf{i'}, \mathbf{j'}), \qquad F_{34}' = F(\mathbf{k'}, \mathbf{l'}),$$

and if we want to learn how to find these components when we know the original components we must express $\mathbf{i'}$, $\mathbf{j'}$, $\mathbf{k'}$, $\mathbf{l'}$ in terms of **i**, **j**, **k**, **l**. Very often it is enough to rotate in one plane at a time. We may, for instance, keep **k** and **l** unchanged and rotate in the **i**-**j** plane so that

$$\mathbf{i'} = \mathbf{i} \cos \theta - \mathbf{j} \sin \theta, \quad \mathbf{j'} = \mathbf{i} \sin \theta + \mathbf{j} \cos \theta, \quad \mathbf{k'} = \mathbf{k}, \quad \mathbf{l'} = \mathbf{l},$$

and

$$F_{12}' = F(\mathbf{i'}, \mathbf{j'}) = F(\mathbf{i} \cos \theta - \mathbf{j} \sin \theta, \mathbf{i} \sin \theta + \mathbf{j} \cos \theta)$$

$$= F(\mathbf{i},\mathbf{i}) \cos \theta \sin \theta + F(\mathbf{i},\mathbf{j}) \cos^2 \theta - F(\mathbf{j},\mathbf{i}) \sin^2 \theta - F(\mathbf{j},\mathbf{j}) \cos \theta \sin \theta.$$

Using relation 10.62 this gives:

$$F_{12}' = F_{12}.$$

In a similar way we can prove the remainder of the following relations:

$$F_{13}' = F(\mathbf{i} \cos \theta - \mathbf{j} \sin \theta, \mathbf{k}) = F_{13} \cos \theta - F_{23} \sin \theta,$$

$$F_{14}' \qquad\qquad\qquad\qquad = F_{14} \cos \theta - F_{24} \sin \theta,$$

$$F_{23}' = F(\mathbf{i} \sin \theta + \mathbf{j} \cos \theta, \mathbf{k}) = F_{13} \sin \theta + F_{23} \cos \theta,$$

$$F_{24}' \qquad\qquad\qquad\qquad = F_{14} \sin \theta + F_{24} \cos \theta,$$

$$F_{34}' = F_{34}.$$

Using the formulas $F_{ij} + F_{ji} = 0$, we note, for further use, that we can write these relations also as

$$F_{12}' = F_{12}, \qquad F_{34}' = F_{34},$$

$$F_{31}' = F_{31} \cos \theta + F_{23} \sin \theta,$$

10.63
$$F_{24}' = F_{24} \cos \theta + F_{14} \sin \theta,$$

$$F_{23}' = F_{23} \cos \theta - F_{31} \sin \theta,$$

$$F_{14}' = F_{14} \cos \theta - F_{24} \sin \theta.$$

We pass now to the consideration of operations on tensors. We have had four such operations: addition, multiplication, contraction, and differentiation.

Addition is defined only for tensors of the same rank (of course, we could add two tensors of different ranks, for instance $\phi(\mathbf{x})$ and $\psi(\mathbf{x}, \mathbf{y})$, considered as *functions*. The sum would be another function; but this function, $\phi(\mathbf{x}) + \psi(\mathbf{x}, \mathbf{y})$ will not be linear in $\mathbf{y}$ and so it will not satisfy the definition of a tensor). The sum of tensors $\phi(\mathbf{x}, \mathbf{y})$ and $\psi(\mathbf{x}, \mathbf{y})$, for instance, is $\phi(\mathbf{x}, \mathbf{y}) + \psi(\mathbf{x}, \mathbf{y})$, and it is easy to see that the components of a sum are equal to the sums of the corresponding components so that the components of the above sum will be

$$\phi_{ij} + \psi_{ij}.$$

It is also easy to see that the product of two tensors of ranks r and s respectively will be a tensor of rank $r + s$ *if the tensors have no argument in common.* Thus $\phi(\mathbf{x}, \mathbf{y}) \cdot \psi(\mathbf{z}, \mathbf{u}, \mathbf{v})$ is a tensor of rank five. Its components are

$$\phi_{ij}\psi_{klm},$$

but $\phi(\mathbf{x}, \mathbf{y}) \cdot \psi(\mathbf{x}, \mathbf{y}, \mathbf{z})$ *is not a tensor.*

Since the product of two tensors of rank one is a tensor of rank two, and the sum of any number of tensors of rank two is a tensor of rank two, we can build tensors of rank two from tensors of rank one.

The question arises whether any tensor of rank two can be built in this way. The answer is given by

Lemma. Any tensor of rank two can be presented as a sum of terms each of which is the product of two tensors of rank one.

Proof. Given a tensor $\omega(\mathbf{x}, \mathbf{y})$, replace $\mathbf{x}$ by its expression (8.2) $\mathbf{x} = \mathbf{e}_i(\mathbf{e}_i x)$ and use linearity. Then

$$\omega(\mathbf{x}, \mathbf{y}) = (\mathbf{e}_1 \mathbf{x}) \cdot \omega(\mathbf{e}_i, \mathbf{y}).$$

This proves the lemma.

Of course, this splitting of a tensor of rank two into a sum of products is not unique. For instance, by using another set of coordinate vectors we would obtain another splitting.

Exercise 6. Prove that any tensor of rank r can be presented as a sum of terms each term being the product of r tensors of rank one.

We are now in a position to discuss a question which must have arisen in the mind of the reader. In the preceding chapter we have agreed to consider a vector as a tensor of rank one. Now, with our new definition of tensor, a vector and a tensor of rank one seem to be entirely different things. However, although they are different there exists a certain correspondence between them; namely, to every *vector* $\mathbf{v}$ we may assign a *tensor of rank one* given by the product of $\mathbf{v}$ by an arbitrary vector $\mathbf{x}$; this product $\mathbf{v} \cdot \mathbf{x}$ is a function of $\mathbf{x}$, and, according to postulate IV (associative and commutative properties), this function is linear (compare 10.6). Since it is a function of one argument (for $\mathbf{v}$ fixed) it is, according to our definition, a tensor of rank one. If we denote this function by $\phi(\mathbf{x})$ the correspondence may be written as

10.7 $\phi(\mathbf{x}) = \mathbf{v} \cdot \mathbf{x}.$

This shows how a ϕ is assigned to every $\mathbf{v}$. Conversely, when a tensor of rank one, $\phi(\mathbf{x})$, is given, we can find the corresponding $\mathbf{v}$; in fact, if we substitute in the above relation for $\mathbf{x}$ the vectors $\mathbf{i}$ and $\mathbf{j}$ in succession we get

$$\mathbf{v} \cdot \mathbf{i} = \phi(\mathbf{i}), \quad \mathbf{v} \cdot \mathbf{j} = \phi(\mathbf{j}),$$

and so we know the components of $\mathbf{v}$ if we know ϕ. We may write

$$\mathbf{v} = \mathbf{i} \cdot \phi(\mathbf{i}) + \mathbf{j} \cdot \phi(\mathbf{j}),$$

and in the general case $\mathbf{v} = \mathbf{e}_i \cdot \phi(\mathbf{e}_i)$. It is easy to show, using postulate V, that $\mathbf{v}$ is uniquely determined by ϕ.

Remark. In some branches of mathematics only addition of vectors and multiplication of vectors by numbers are considered (and not inner multiplication of vectors); in other words, postulates IV and V are omitted. No correspondence can then be established (i.e., no correspondence which can be characterized in terms of relations appearing in the postulates) between vectors and what we call here tensors of rank one.

Next comes the operation of contraction. We have defined it in terms of components and indices (p. 12) before we had a valid definition of a tensor. We must justify it now by showing that it gives a result independent of the choice of the coordinate system. To do this we use the above lemma which says that a tensor of rank two is a sum of products of tensors of rank one, so that we may write

10.8 $$\omega(\mathbf{x}, \mathbf{y}) = \Sigma\phi(\mathbf{x}) \cdot \psi(\mathbf{y}).$$

We also know that the tensors of rank one ϕ and ψ may each be written as an inner product of a constant vector by the argument, so that

$$\omega(\mathbf{x}, \mathbf{y}) = \Sigma(\mathbf{u}\mathbf{x})(\mathbf{v}\mathbf{y}).$$

Now if we introduce an operation which replaces the above by the sum of products of the corresponding $\mathbf{u}$ and $\mathbf{v}$, that is

$$\Sigma\mathbf{u}\mathbf{v},$$

we have an operation defined independently of the coordinate system, because it was defined without using a specific coordinate system. We will show that it is the same operation as the operation of contraction defined before. In fact, using coordinates we know that $\mathbf{u} \cdot \mathbf{v} = u_iv_i$, and since we know that the components of ϕ and ψ are the same as the components of $\mathbf{u}$ and $\mathbf{v}$ we may write the above as

$$\Sigma\phi_i\psi_i.$$

But relation 10.8 may be written in components as $\omega_{ij} = \Sigma\phi_i\psi_j$, so that the above expression is ω_{ii}, which was the original definition. (Incidentally, the result shows that the definition does not depend on the method of decomposition of ω into the sum of products.)

For skew-symmetric tensors in four-space in addition to the operations of addition and multiplication, which apply to all tensors, a special operation can be defined called the formation of the dual. If such a tensor is given by its components F_{ij} the dual D_{ij} is defined as follows:

10.64 $$D_{12} = F_{34}, \quad D_{23} = F_{14}, \quad D_{31} = F_{24},$$
$$D_{34} = F_{12}, \quad D_{14} = F_{23}, \quad D_{24} = F_{31}.$$

In order to show that this operation which is defined through the use of a special coordinate system really does not depend on what coordinate system we are using we must show that the above relations hold for all system of coordinates, i.e., that they are not affected by a transformation of coordinates. Since any coordinate transformation may be achieved by consecutive transformations, each of which affects only two coordinate vectors, i.e., rotations in one of the coordinate planes, all we have to do is to observe what happens to the above relations as the result of such rotations. But a glance at formulas 10.63 will show that they are not affected by the transformation.

We have proved, therefore, that relations 10.64 and therefore the definition of a dual are invariant.

Exercise 7. Prove that the dual of the dual of a skew-symmetric tensor F is that tensor itself.

Exercise 8. Referring to the geometrical interpretation of a skew-symmetric tensor (p. 29), find the geometrical meaning of the dual.

So far we have considered what are properly called tensors, or we could say *constant* tensors. The next operation we want to discuss, the operation of differentiation, applies to *tensor fields*. We have a tensor field if we have a tensor in every point of space or every point of a certain region of space. In general, then, we have different tensors in different points of the region, so that we can speak of variable tensors. Since, however, a tensor itself is a function of vectors it may be better to say that a tensor field is a function which in addition to its (linear) dependence on vector arguments depends also on a point argument. If we imagine a coordinate system in our space, the tensor in every point will have components and these components will be functions of the coordinates. As far as notation is concerned this dependence of the tensor components on the coordinates is usually not explicitly indicated, so that we write ϕ_{ij} and assume that these quantities are functions of x, y, z, t.

We will begin with the simplest case, that of a tensor field of order zero, or a scalar field. This means simply that we have a function of the coordinates. In two dimensions this is just a function f of two variables, x and y. We assume that this function has partial derivatives and write its differential as

$$df = \frac{\partial f}{\partial x}\, dx + \frac{\partial f}{\partial y}\, dy,$$

or, using index notation, as

$$df = \partial_1 f \cdot dx_1 + \partial_2 f \cdot dx_2.$$

This is a function of four variables: namely, x, y on which $\partial f/\partial x$, $\partial f/\partial y$ depend, and the new variables dx, dy which are called "the differentials of the independent variables." Let us, for the moment, fix the values of x and y. Then df is a function of dx and dy. The same applies, of course, to a function of any number of variables and *its* differential. If we interpret the variables as cartesian coordinates in a plane (or in Euclidean space of any number of dimensions), the differentials of the independent variables are the components of a vector. The differential appears then as a linear function of the components of a vector and therefore of the vector; it is, according to our definition, a *tensor* (of rank one). The partial derivatives appear then as the *components* of that tensor. The advantage of considering the differential of a function of several variables rather than its partial derivatives is similar to the advantage of considering the tensor rather than its components, in that the differential as a definite function of a vector is independent of the choice of variables. This is true in this sense: if we pass from the original coordinates to coordinates in another coordinate system, i.e., express f in new coordinates, the derivatives will change, i.e., the partial derivatives with respect to the new coordinate system will be different, but the *differential* will be the same; i.e., df will have the same values (for the same vector argument which of course will be given by different components, namely the differentials of the new variables). The last statement can be proved by a simple calculation based on the transformation formulas 10.2. If we restore the variability to x and y (which were fixed, up to now) we have a tensor df in each point, i.e., a tensor field.

Next we pass to the differentiation of a tensor field of rank one. In components the tensor field $\phi(\mathbf{v})$ will be written as $\phi_1 v_1 + \phi_2 v_2$, where ϕ_1 and ϕ_2 are functions of the coordinates x_1 and x_2. In finding the differential of this we consider v_1 and v_2 constant; that is, we differentiate $\phi(\mathbf{v})$ as if it were a function of x_1 and x_2 only, and have in this way

$$d\phi(\mathbf{v}) = d(\phi_1 v_1 + \phi_2 v_2) = \partial_1\phi_1 \cdot v_1\, dx_1 + \partial_2\phi_1 \cdot v_1\, dx_2 + \partial_1\phi_2 \cdot v_2\, dx_1$$
$$+ \partial_2\phi_2 \cdot v_2\, dx_2.$$

Then, restoring variability to v_1 and v_2, we have, we may say, a function of six variables. The result depends on v_1 and v_2 linearly, on dx_1 and dx_2 also linearly, and (through ϕ_1 and ϕ_2) on x_1 and x_2. In other words we have for each point (x_1, x_2) a tensor with the two vectors dx_1, dx_2 and v_1, v_2 as vector arguments, that is a tensor field of rank two. It may be, of course, that the tensor field $\phi(v)$ was itself obtained by differentiating a tensor field f of rank zero. Then ϕ_1 and ϕ_2 are the partial derivatives $\partial_1 f$ and $\partial_2 f$, and the components v_1 and v_2 of $\mathbf{v}$ are differentials of the independent variables, but they are not to be considered the same as dx_1, dx_2. We must use some other notation to keep these two sets of differentials of the independent variables apart. Very often the letter δ is used for this purpose, and so we write δx_1, δx_2 for the components of $\mathbf{v}$ and

$$d\phi(\mathbf{v}) = d\,\delta f = \partial_1\partial_1 f \cdot \delta x_1\,dx_1 + \partial_2\partial_1 f \cdot \delta x_1\,dx_2$$
$$+ \partial_1\partial_2 f \cdot \delta x_2\,dx_1 + \partial_2\partial_2 f \cdot \delta x_2\,dx_2.$$

This is the second differential of f; it is a tensor of rank two; the second partial derivatives $\partial_i\partial_j f$ are its components. We said before that δx_i are not the same as dx_i. This does not mean, of course, that we have no right to set $dx_i = \delta x_i$; we obtain, if we do this, a quadratic form instead of the bilinear form written out before.

In general, we may differentiate in this way a tensor of rank r (which itself may have been obtained by differentiations of a tensor of lower rank) and obtain a tensor of rank $r + 1$. Each differentiation increases the rank of a tensor field by 1, adding a new vector argument whose components are a new set of differentials of the independent variables. As far as components are concerned each differentiation increases the number of indices by 1.

REMARK. In four dimensions we will usually perform rotations in one plane at a time, but it is easy to see how (in four or n dimensions) the general formulas of transformation of coordinates apply to tensors. Given the components ϕ_{ik} of a tensor of rank two we consider them as $\phi(\mathbf{e}_i, \mathbf{e}_k)$. Replacing $\mathbf{e}_i$, $\mathbf{e}_k$ by their expressions in the new coordinate vectors 8.4, and using linearity, we obtain

$$\phi(a_{ik}\mathbf{e}_k', a_{js}\mathbf{e}_s') = a_{ik}a_{js}\phi(\mathbf{e}_k', \mathbf{e}_s'),$$

so that

$$\phi_{ij} = a_{ik}a_{js}\phi_{ks}'.$$

Analogous formulas can be obtained which express ϕ_{ks}' in terms of ϕ_{ij}. The coefficients then involve the coefficients of the expressions of $\mathbf{e}_j'$ in terms of $\mathbf{e}_i$. We will have to discuss these transformations in more detail in section 25.

11. Complications resulting from imaginary coordinate

An imaginary coordinate was originally used just as a device that permitted us to write certain formulas in a compact way. *Logically* writing formulas in this form does not alter their content. The formulas written with the use of imaginary notation say exactly the same thing as the formulas from which they have been obtained—it is like translating a statement from one language to another. However, *psychologically*, using the notation x_i for x, y, z, ti implies that we are treating these quantities as if they were coordinates in a four-space. In particular, it implies that we can form, and expect to find a meaning for, expressions and formulas that are analogous to expressions and formulas of solid analytic geometry. The most important of these are the expression for the distance between two points and the formulas of transformation of coordinates. The implication of using an imaginary component in these formulas, or, to put it another way, the implication of applying formulas analogous to those of solid analytic geometry to the quantities x_i considered as coordinates, is somewhat hidden by the fact that the new formulas look like the familiar geometrical formulas. It is true that sometimes it is convenient to forget that x_4 and certain other quantities are imaginary, as when we want to derive formal consequences from given formulas; but when it comes to physical interpretation it becomes important to bring to light these hidden implications.

This section is mainly devoted to the task of discussing the hidden implications of the two formulas mentioned above: the distance formula and the formula for transformation of coordinates.

A space with one imaginary coordinate is often called a *Minkowski* space. We begin, according to our plan formulated in the beginning of Chapter 2, by the consideration of a *three*-dimensional Minkowski space. We assume that all formulas of ordinary analytic geometry hold but that one coordinate is imaginary. In order not to have to change our notation later, when we come to the consideration of four-dimensional space, we will denote the real coordinates by x_2, x_3 and the imaginary coordinate by x_4. We begin by considering the expression for the square of the distance between two points:

$$(x_2 - x_2')^2 + (x_3 - x_3')^2 + (x_4 - x_4')^2.$$

Since x_4 and x_4' are imaginary the sign of the last term is negative and the expression may, depending on the relative magnitude of the terms, be positive, negative, or zero. There must therefore be three types of relative position of two points, three types of directions and vectors; namely, there must be vectors of positive square, those of negative square, and those of zero square.

It is not necessary, but if we want to develop something of an intuitive grasp of the situation it is desirable, to make use of the intuition we have for handling ordinary three-dimensional space. We consider therefore together with every "point" of our Minkowski space of coordinates x_2, x_3, x_4 a point of our ordinary space of coordinates x_2, x_3, and x_4/i, or y, z, t.   We remark that we use this ordinary space only as a schematic map, or a model, or a diagram, of the space we actually have in mind; that is, we are not using, and therefore should try to disregard, some properties of the model: we must learn to distinguish between those properties of our model that have, and those that have not, significance for the space we wish to represent.   A point in the model represents a point in the Minkowski space; a vector in the model represents a vector in that space; a plane represents a plane, but the statement that two vectors are perpendicular to each other in the model has no significance for the space.   The vectors of the Minkowski space represented by two perpendicular vectors of the model may or may not be perpendicular.   Also the length of a vector of the model has nothing to do with the length of the Minkowski space vector represented by it.

Limiting ourselves to vectors with initial point at the origin we consider first in detail the vectors of zero square, i.e., vectors for which we have $u_2{}^2 + u_3{}^2 + u_4{}^2 = 0$, or introducing v, w, and q for u_2, u_3, and u_4/i,

$$v^2 + w^2 - q^2 = 0.$$

This is in the model the equation of a certain circular cone; vectors (with initial point at the origin) which lie on the generators of that cone represent therefore vectors of zero square.   It is easy to see that those vectors that are in the interior of the cone, for example, the vectors $(0, 0, 1)$ and $(0, 0, -1)$ of the model, represent vectors of negative square.   The interior of the cone consists of two funnels, and so vectors of negative square fall into two separate classes: those that are in one and those that are in the other of these two funnels.   Finally those vectors that are in the model outside the cone (but still have the origin at the vertex) are of positive square.

If we are given two vectors of the Minkowski space by their components u_2, u_3, u_4 and u_2', u_3', u_4', their (inner) product will be given by $u_2u_2' + u_3u_3' + u_4u_4'$, so that we have the expression

$$vv' + ww' - qq'$$

for the inner product of the vectors expressed in real components. We shall say that two vectors are "perpendicular" if their "product" is zero.   The example of the vector 0, 1, 1 shows that here a vector *may be "perpendicular" to itself*.   (This is one of the previously hidden implications of the use of imaginary coordinates.)   All the zero-square vectors are self-perpendicular, and it is easy to see that any self-perpendicular vector has a zero square; i.e., its image in the model lies on the cone. We will prove later (see lemma on p. 55) that if a vector belongs to the interior of the cone any vector "perpendicular" to it lies outside the cone.

Exercise 1. Find the locus of points "equidistant" from the origin. Consider the cases when the square of that distance is positive, negative, and zero.

In order to arrive in a natural way at the coordinate transformations, we consider, as we did in section 8, the representation of a vector as linear combinations of three fixed vectors. The peculiarities introduced in this section do not affect such representations in general, for any vector is a linear combination of three independent vectors. However, if we want to use an "orthonormal" set we must revise our idea of a unit vector.

Given any vector of positive square, we can find a vector of the same direction and of "length" unity; all we have to do is to divide the vector, i.e., all its components, by the square root of its "square." If a vector is of negative "square" all the vectors of the same direction will also be of negative "square," and so we *cannot* find a vector of the same direction of "square" 1, because multiplication of a vector by a scalar, i.e., by a real number, will result in the multiplication of its square by a positive number. But we *can* find one of "square" -1. For that purpose we have to divide the vector by the square root of the absolute value of its "square." In both cases we will *agree to call the resulting vector a unit vector—we can say that a "unit vector" is one whose "square" is ± 1.* If a vector is of zero "square," all vectors of the same direction are also of zero "square" and there is no unit vector in that direction.

An example of an orthonormal set in this new sense is given by the vectors $\mathbf{j} = (1, 0, 0)$, $\mathbf{k} = (0, 1, 0)$, $\mathbf{l} = (0, 0, 1)$. They are all "unit vectors": the first two have "squares" equal to $+1$; the "square" of the last is -1. If we express any vector $\mathbf{v}$ as a linear combination of these three vectors the coefficients of that linear combination will be the (real) original components of the vector; i.e.,

$$\mathbf{v} = v\mathbf{j} + w\mathbf{k} + q\mathbf{l}.$$

The formula

$$\mathbf{v}^2 = v^2 + w^2 - q^2$$

results from the fact that $\mathbf{l}^2 = -1$. Of course, as in section 8, we can use in the same way any other set of three "orthonormal vectors," orthonormal in the new sense. The fact that this particular set $\mathbf{j}$, $\mathbf{k}$, $\mathbf{l}$ is orthonormal in both senses, i.e., that they as well as their images in the model are orthonormal, may be a little confusing. The example of another orthonormal set, $(1, 0, 0)$, $(0, \frac{5}{4}, \frac{3}{4})$, and $(0, \frac{3}{4}, \frac{5}{4})$, in which the last two vectors are "unit vectors" and "perpendicular" in the sense of the Minkowski space but *not* in the sense of the model shows that this does not happen always.   Let us find now how to obtain, in general, any orthonormal set from a given orthonormal set. The procedure is very similar to one we followed in section 8, but we are not using the index notation here, and we must be more careful because we are not on familiar ground.   Consider the orthonormal sets $\mathbf{j}, \mathbf{k}, \mathbf{l}$ and $\mathbf{j}', \mathbf{k}', \mathbf{l}'$.   We can write

$$\mathbf{j}' = \lambda_2\mathbf{j} + \mu_2\mathbf{k} + \nu_2\mathbf{l},$$

11.1 $$\mathbf{k}' = \lambda_3\mathbf{j} + \mu_3\mathbf{k} + \nu_3\mathbf{l},$$

$$\mathbf{l}' = \lambda_4\mathbf{j} + \mu_4\mathbf{k} + \nu_4\mathbf{l}.$$

Using the fact that $\mathbf{j}, \mathbf{k}, \mathbf{l}$ form an orthonormal set, that is that $\mathbf{j}^2 = 1$, $\mathbf{k}^2 = 1$, $\mathbf{l}^2 = -1$, $\mathbf{j} \cdot \mathbf{k} = 0$, $\mathbf{j} \cdot \mathbf{l} = 0$, $\mathbf{k} \cdot \mathbf{l} = 0$, and that the vectors $\mathbf{j}', \mathbf{k}'$, and $\mathbf{l}'$ are perpendicular in pairs, we arrive at the relations

11.2 $$\lambda_2\lambda_3 + \mu_2\mu_3 - \nu_2\nu_3 = 0, \quad \lambda_2\lambda_4 + \mu_2\mu_4 - \nu_2\nu_4 = 0,$$

$$\lambda_3\lambda_4 + \mu_3\mu_4 - \nu_3\nu_4 = 0.$$

Before we continue we must raise this question: of the three vectors $\mathbf{j}, \mathbf{k}, \mathbf{l}$, two had squares $+1$ and one the square -1.   We want $\mathbf{j}'$, $\mathbf{k}'$, $\mathbf{l}'$ to form an orthonormal set.   They must therefore be perpendicular in pairs (we took this fact into account in deriving the above formulas) but they also must be unit vectors.   Since unit vector now means that the square is $+$ *or* -1, are we free to decide whether we want $\mathbf{j}', \mathbf{k}', \mathbf{l}'$ to be positive square or negative square unit vectors? It is easy to see that they could not be all positive square or all negative square vectors because then all their linear combinations and therefore *all* vectors would be of positive square or of negative square respectively.   But could it be that two of them are of negative square and one of positive square?   Could we have, for example,

$$\mathbf{j}'^2 = 1, \quad \mathbf{k}'^2 = -1, \quad \mathbf{l}'^2 = -1?$$

To settle this question we will prove the following:

LEMMA.   Two perpendicular vectors in a Minkowski space cannot both be of negative square.

Proof.   Denote the components of the two vectors by v, w, q and v', w', q'.   Then perpendicularity is expressed by

$$vv' + ww' = qq'.$$

We can always make $v = 0$ by rotation in the y-z plane. Then this equation reduces to $ww' = qq'$. Squaring, we get

$$w^2 w'^2 = q^2 q'^2.$$

If the first vector has negative square, then

$$w^2 < q^2.$$

We therefore must have $w'^2 > q'^2$, and this shows that the square of the second vector, $v'^2 + w'^2 - q'^2$, cannot be negative. The lemma is proved.

Thus one of the vectors $\mathbf{j}'$, $\mathbf{k}'$, $\mathbf{l}'$ must be of negative square and two of positive square. Let us make $\mathbf{j}'^2 = 1$, $\mathbf{k}'^2 = 1$, $\mathbf{l}'^2 = -1$. We can now return to the determination of the coefficients λ, μ, ν, and we find by a calculation similar to the one which led us to formulas 11.2 that

11.21 $\qquad \lambda_2^2 + \mu_2^2 - \nu_2^2 = 1, \quad \lambda_3^2 + \mu_3^2 - \nu_3^2 = 1,$

$$\lambda_4^2 + \mu_4^2 - \nu_4^2 = -1.$$

The six formulas 11.2 and 11.21 take the place of the relations on the direction cosines appearing in the formulas for transformation of coordinates in solid analytic geometry. Of course, the minus signs that appear in these formulas can be traced to the minus-sign difficulty (p. 15) which arose in connection with the Maxwell equations. The introduction of an imaginary coordinate may be looked upon as a temporary device which has led us from those minus signs to these.

Transformations of coordinates in Minkowski space differ in one important respect from transformations in ordinary (Euclidean) space. There, when we say that the three vectors $\mathbf{j}$, $\mathbf{k}$, $\mathbf{l}$ are replaced by $\mathbf{j}'$, $\mathbf{k}'$, $\mathbf{l}'$, it makes no sense to say that $\mathbf{j}$ is necessarily replaced by $\mathbf{j}'$, $\mathbf{k}$ by $\mathbf{k}'$, etc., because all these vectors are of the same kind. They do not differ from each other in any essential properties. We could just as well say that $\mathbf{j}$ is replaced by $\mathbf{k}'$, $\mathbf{k}$ by $\mathbf{j}'$. Not so in Minkowski space. We know that one of the vectors in each orthonormal set is in the interior of the cone. It makes sense to say then that $\mathbf{l}$ goes into $\mathbf{l}'$ if $\mathbf{l}$ and $\mathbf{l}'$ are the ones that are inside the cone. We have assumed this in deriving the transformation formulas, and we will always do that. Furthermore, we can specify that $\mathbf{l}$ and $\mathbf{l}'$ must be *in the same funnel* of the cone. This obviously means that the inner product $\mathbf{l} \cdot \mathbf{l}'$ is negative, that is, that ν_4 *should be positive*.

The following two exercises exhibit situations that have no counterpart in Euclidean space.

Exercise 2. Show that the numbers

$$\begin{array}{ccc} 1 & -\beta & \beta \\[4pt] \beta & 1 - \tfrac{1}{2}\beta^2 & \tfrac{1}{2}\beta^2 \\[4pt] \beta & -\tfrac{1}{2}\beta^2 & 1 + \tfrac{1}{2}\beta^2 \end{array}$$

satisfy equations 11.2 and 11.21.

Exercise 3. Show that the numbers

$$\begin{array}{ccc} 1 + \beta^2 & \beta\gamma & \beta\delta \\[4pt] \gamma\beta & 1 + \gamma^2 & \gamma\delta \\[4pt] \delta\beta & \delta\gamma & \delta^2 - 1 \end{array}$$

with $\beta^2 + \gamma^2 - \delta^2 = -2$ satisfy the same equations.

As in the Euclidean space, a general transformation of coordinates in the Minkowski space can be achieved by a succession of transformations each involving only two vectors. But here, if we use real components, we must distinguish two different cases. If both vectors to be replaced are of positive square we have exactly the same situation as we had before and the transformation formulas are given by equation 8.7,* but if one of the vectors is of negative square the formulas will be different. They may be obtained from equations 11.1 by making $\lambda_2 = 1$, $\mu_2 = \nu_2 = \lambda_3 = \lambda_4 = 0$. The restriction 11.2 reduces to

$$\mu_3\mu_4 - \nu_3\nu_4 = 0,$$

while that of 11.2 becomes

$$\mu_3{}^2 - \nu_3{}^2 = 1, \quad \mu_4{}^2 - \nu_4{}^2 = -1.$$

The last two relations may be written as $\mu_3{}^2 = \nu_3{}^2 + 1, 1 + \mu_4{}^2 = \nu_4{}^2$.

Multiplying these equations together and taking account of the first we get $\mu_3{}^2 = \nu_4{}^2$, and similarly we have $\mu_4{}^2 = \nu_3{}^2$. Denoting ν_4, which must be positive, by σ, and ν_3 by $-\tau$, we can write the transformation as

11.3
$$\begin{aligned} \mathbf{k}' &= \sigma\mathbf{k} - \tau\mathbf{l}, \\ \mathbf{l}' &= -\tau\mathbf{k} + \sigma\mathbf{l}, \end{aligned} \quad \text{or} \quad \begin{aligned} \mathbf{k}' &= -\sigma\mathbf{k} - \tau\mathbf{l}, \\ \mathbf{l}' &= \tau\mathbf{k} + \sigma\mathbf{l}, \end{aligned}$$

with $\sigma^2 - \tau^2 = 1$ and $\sigma > 0$.

We will never have occasion to use the second set (which goes into the first by changing the sign of $\mathbf{k}$). If we want to express σ and τ in terms of one parameter (in analogy to Euclidean rotation) we can set

* We have used this fact in the proof of the lemma.

11.31 $\sigma = \sec \psi,$ $\tau = \tan \psi,$ $-\dfrac{\pi}{2} < \psi < \dfrac{\pi}{2},$

although no geometrical meaning is ascribed to ψ. We will refer to transformations 11.3 as *pseudo-rotations* of the axes. If we want to know how the components of a vector are transformed as a result of such a pseudo-rotation we can write a vector **v**, using both sets of axes, as

$$\mathbf{v} = w\mathbf{k} + q\mathbf{l} = w'\mathbf{k}' + q'\mathbf{l}'.$$

Substituting for $\mathbf{k}'$ and $\mathbf{l}'$ their expressions 11.3, we find

$$w = \sigma w' - \tau q', \quad q = -\tau w' + \sigma q'.$$

Solving these, we obtain

11.32 $w' = \sigma w + \tau q, \quad q' = \tau w + \sigma q.$

Exercise 4. Show that a pseudo-rotation, unlike an ordinary rotation, does not change the direction of certain vectors. Does it change their lengths?

According to our plan, the next step will be to pass to the space in which points are represented by *four* coordinates, one of which is imaginary. Here we cannot use our three-dimensional space with a cone in it as a model, but the situation is very similar, and we can try by analogy to speak of a cone in four-space whose equation is

$$u^2 + v^2 + w^2 - q^2 = 0.$$

It can be expected that the vectors will be of three types—those of positive square, those of zero square, and those of negative square—and that the last will fall into two classes according to the funnel of the cone in which they are. For these conclusions we are relying on an analogy which, conceivably, might be misleading.

Even in three-dimensional space with one imaginary coordinate, although using ordinary three-dimensional space as a model might have helped us as far as intuition is concerned, we were logically on somewhat shaky ground, and here we feel even more the lack of a firm foundation. In four-dimensional space with all real coordinates we found such a firm foundation in a postulational formulation, and now we want to do the same here. (A reader who feels that he is on safe ground already need not follow us in this.) Our system of postulates has been chosen in such a way that only a slight modification is needed in order to obtain a basis for four-dimensional space with one imaginary coordinate; this modification concerns postulate V (p. 37) and is suggested by the lemma which we proved above on the basis of our preliminary consideration. The new postulate will be

POSTULATE V'. There exists a vector of negative square; a non-zero vector perpendicular to a vector of negative square is of positive square.

Accepting this postulate we must now reverse our steps and derive from it the propositions that we, so to say, guessed at and that led us to the formulation of the postulate.

The vectors of negative square fall into two distinct classes. In the three-dimensional case we derived this by using our model. This circumstance is of great importance, and for that reason we want to give it a formal proof based on postulates, which is applicable independently of the number of dimensions.* Consider three independent vectors of negative squares: $\mathbf{a}, \mathbf{b}, \mathbf{c}$. Form the vector

$$\mathbf{x} = \mathbf{a}(\mathbf{bc}) - \mathbf{b}(\mathbf{ac}).$$

Multiplying this by $\mathbf{c}$ we find that $\mathbf{x}$ is perpendicular to $\mathbf{c}$, and thus, according to postulate V', $\mathbf{x}$ is a vector of positive square; in other words,

$$\mathbf{x}^2 = \mathbf{a}^2(\mathbf{bc})^2 - 2(\mathbf{ab}) \cdot (\mathbf{bc}) \cdot (\mathbf{ac}) + \mathbf{b}^2(\mathbf{ac})^2$$

is a positive number, and since $\mathbf{a}^2$ and $\mathbf{b}^2$ are negative, this means

$$(\mathbf{ab}) \cdot (\mathbf{bc}) \cdot (\mathbf{ac}) < 0.$$

This shows that *if* $\mathbf{ab}$ *and* $\mathbf{ac}$ *are negative then* $\mathbf{bc}$ *is also negative.* Now we can establish the fact that vectors of negative square are divided into two distinct categories, two funnels of the cone, in a formal way without using the analogy with and the intuition of our ordinary three-space. We define two vectors of negative square as equivalent if their inner product is negative. The italicized statement above implies the transitivity of this relation, so that the vectors of negative square are divided into equivalence classes. Since the same inequality also implies that two vectors of negative square which are not equivalent to a given vector are equivalent to each other, there are only two equivalence classes.

We have now come closer to the resolution of the conflict between our intuition and our formulas mentioned before at the end of section 7. In physical interpretation the positive square vectors correspond to space dimension and those of negative square to time. (They are often referred to as space-like and time-like respectively.) They can be treated alike in many respects, but they are different in that they

---

* This proof is due to J. B. Wright.

have squares of different sign. Moreover, unlike the situation in Euclidean spaces, coordinate transformations never take a space-like vector into a time-like one, or vice versa. Finally, the time-like vectors are divided into two distinct categories or funnels, corresponding to the distinction between past and future (this property of time is sometimes called irreversibility, a distinction that has no counterpart either in Euclidean space or in space-like vectors of the Minkowski space).

Since we have established a firm foundation for our geometry there is no difficulty in discussing coordinates and their transformations. We begin with orthonormal sets, and we know that such a set cannot consist of vectors of positive square only. On the other hand, we know that there exists a vector of negative square, and that by dividing it by the absolute value of its square we obtain a unit vector $\mathbf{l}$ of negative square. We know that all non-zero vectors perpendicular to it have a positive square. They satisfy, therefore, all the postulates of section 9 except that the number of dimensions of the space they constitute is three instead of four. By the reasoning used there we can prove that that space contains an orthonormal set of three vectors which we denote by $\mathbf{i}, \mathbf{j}, \mathbf{k}$, and consequently that the vectors $\mathbf{i}, \mathbf{j}, \mathbf{k}, \mathbf{l}$ constitute an orthonormal set for our four-dimensional Minkowski space.

The transformation formulas are analogous to 11.1 and will be written as

$$\mathbf{i}' = \lambda_{11}\mathbf{i} + \lambda_{12}\mathbf{j} + \lambda_{13}\mathbf{k} + \lambda_{14}\mathbf{l},$$

11.4
$$\mathbf{j}' = \lambda_{21}\mathbf{i} + \lambda_{22}\mathbf{j} + \lambda_{23}\mathbf{k} + \lambda_{24}\mathbf{l},$$

$$\mathbf{k}' = \lambda_{31}\mathbf{i} + \lambda_{32}\mathbf{j} + \lambda_{33}\mathbf{k} + \lambda_{34}\mathbf{l},$$

$$\mathbf{l}' = \lambda_{41}\mathbf{i} + \lambda_{42}\mathbf{j} + \lambda_{43}\mathbf{k} + \lambda_{44}\mathbf{l}.$$

The restrictions on the coefficients can be derived in a way similar to that used in deriving 11.2, 11.21. These restrictions are

$$\lambda_{11}^2 + \lambda_{12}^2 + \lambda_{13}^2 - \lambda_{14}^2 = 1,$$

$$\lambda_{11}\lambda_{21} + \lambda_{12}\lambda_{22} + \lambda_{13}\lambda_{23} - \lambda_{14}\lambda_{24} = 0, \quad \cdots$$

11.5
$$\lambda_{41}^2 + \lambda_{42}^2 + \lambda_{43}^2 - \lambda_{44}^2 = -1,$$

and

$$\lambda_{44} > 0.$$

Transformation of vector components is given by similar formulas.

Exercise 5.   Prove that the transformation with coefficients

$$
\begin{array}{cccc}
1 & 0 & -a & a \\[6pt]
0 & 1 & -b & b \\[6pt]
a & b & 1 - \dfrac{a^2 + b^2}{2} & \dfrac{a^2 + b^2}{2} \\[12pt]
a & b & -\dfrac{a^2 + b^2}{2} & 1 + \dfrac{a^2 + b^2}{2}
\end{array}
$$

satisfies 11.5.

Exercise 6.   Prove that the above transformation does not change the vector $(0, 0, 1, 1)$.

Exercise 7.   Find a transformation of a Minkowski four-space analogous to that of exercise 3 of this section.

Now that we have derived the coordinate transformation formulas using only real numbers we may ask whether these formulas, like Maxwell's equations, also could be more simply written by the use of imaginary numbers in the proper places.   The answer is that they can. If in the above formulas we replace λ_{14} by ib_{14}, λ_{24} by ib_{24}, λ_{34} by ib_{34}, λ_{41} by $-ib_{41}$, λ_{42} by $-ib_{42}$, λ_{43} by $-ib_{43}$, the other λ_{ij} by b_{ij}, and, of course, use u_1, u_2, u_3 for u, v, w and u_4 for iq, then one transformation formula will be

$$
u_1{}' = \lambda_{11}u_1 + \lambda_{12}u_2 + \lambda_{13}u_3 + ib_{14}\frac{u_4}{i} = b_{1j}u_j.
$$

Similar formulas hold for $u_2{}'$ and $u_3{}'$, and

$$
u_4{}' = iq' = i\left(-ib_{41}u_1 - ib_{42}u_2 - ib_{43}u_3 + b_{44}\frac{u_4}{i}\right) = b_{4j}u_4,
$$

so that we can write

$$
u_i{}' = b_{ij}u_j,
$$

and the relations 11.5 take the form

11.51 $b_{ij}b_{ik} = \delta_{jk},$

which is formally the same as for Euclidean space, although now we know what is concealed behind these simple formulas.   We wish to emphasize again that this simplicity, and the analogy that these formulas seem to exhibit with the corresponding formulas for ordinary space, are misleading.   That the simplicity is misleading is shown by the existence of the transformations of special types brought out in exercises 2, 3, 5, and 7; that the analogy is misleading is shown by the fact that in the ordinary case any axis can be changed into any axis, whereas in the pseudo-Euclidean case the time axis, although it is not fixed, cannot be brought into a space axis by any transformation, nor can the sense on it be reversed. Thus we see again how the conflict mentioned before has to be resolved. Although formally we may treat the space coordinates and the time multiplied by i in the same way, the fact that we had to multiply by i in order to be able to do so results in fundamental differences that correspond to the differences in our intuition.

We have written down the general transformation 11.4 mainly for the sake of completeness. In practical applications it is usually sufficient to change, as we have mentioned before, only two unit vectors at a time. We shall now give an example of such an application. We know how the representation of a symmetric tensor can be simplified in the ordinary Euclidean plane (p. 42) by choosing a coordinate system in which $a_{12} = a_{21} = 0$. In view of a very important application later (in section 19) we want to investigate now whether such a simplification is possible in a Minkowski plane, that means when one of the coordinates is real and the other imaginary.

At first glance the situation seems to be similar to that in the ordinary plane, but this is one of those places in which the use of imaginary coordinates obscures the situation. If the tensor is $\phi(\mathbf{x}, \mathbf{y})$, and its components using the coordinate vectors $\mathbf{k}$ and $\mathbf{l}$ with $\mathbf{k}^2 = 1$, $\mathbf{k} \cdot \mathbf{l} = 0, \mathbf{l}^2 = -1$ are

$$A = \phi(\mathbf{k}, \mathbf{k}), \qquad B = \phi(\mathbf{k}, \mathbf{l}) = \phi(\mathbf{l}, \mathbf{k}), \qquad C = \phi(\mathbf{l}, \mathbf{l}),$$

we want to find another orthonormal set $\mathbf{k}'$, $\mathbf{l}'$ such that in the new system $B' = 0$. More in detail, we want to find σ and τ with $\sigma > 0$ and $\sigma^2 - \tau^2 = 1$ in such a way that if we set

$$\mathbf{k}' = \sigma\mathbf{k} - \tau\mathbf{l}, \qquad \mathbf{l}' = -\tau\mathbf{k} + \sigma\mathbf{l},$$

we obtain $\phi(\mathbf{k}', \mathbf{l}') = 0$ or

$$\phi(\sigma\mathbf{k} - \tau\mathbf{l}, -\tau\mathbf{k} + \sigma\mathbf{l}) = -\sigma\tau A + (\sigma^2 + \tau^2)B - \sigma\tau C = 0.$$

Dividing by σ^2 we obtain (compare 11.31)

$$B \sin^2 \psi - (A + C) \sin \psi + B = 0.$$

The product of the roots of this equation is 1, and so, if the roots are real and distinct, one of them is necessarily less than 1 in absolute value and this must be the value of $\sin \psi$. The condition for real, distinct roots is

11.6 $\quad \Delta = (A + C)^2 - 4B^2 = (A + C - 2B)(A + C + 2B) > 0.$

If this condition is not satisfied either because $\Delta = 0$ or because $\Delta < 0$, there is no transformation that will result in $B' = 0$ or, as we say, in the diagonalization of the array or matrix,

$$A \quad B$$
$$B \quad C.$$

Sometimes it is convenient when only two coordinates are involved to use imaginary numbers in the same way as we did above in the general case. Writing the formulas

$$u' = \sigma u + \tau q, \qquad q' = \tau u + \sigma q, \qquad \sigma^2 - \tau^2 = 1,$$

as

$$u' = \sigma u - i\tau \cdot iq, \qquad iq' = i\tau \cdot u + \sigma \cdot iq, \qquad \sigma^2 + (i\tau)^2 = 1,$$

and using index notation, we have

11.7 $$u_3' = \sigma u_3 - i\tau u_4, \qquad u_4' = i\tau u_3 + \sigma u_4.$$

Now we can formally write

11.8 $$\sigma = \cos \theta, \qquad i\tau = \sin \theta.$$

The formulas assume the form of the usual rotation formulas in the plane (here, however, θ is imaginary) so that we can use formulas of the same form in all the planes. This is very convenient if, for example, we want to prove the invariance of some expression or relation. Since a general rotation can be achieved by successive rotations in single planes, and since the rotation formulas are the same for all planes, it is enough to prove invariance under such a rotation in one plane.

We want to derive now transformation formulas for the components of a skew-symmetric tensor under pseudo-rotations. Using imaginary numbers the formulas of transformation corresponding to a rotation in the 3-4 plane are the same as formulas 10.63 corresponding to a rotation in the 1-2 plane. Interchanging the indices 1, 2 and 3, 4 we can write

$$F'_{12} = F_{12}, \qquad F'_{34} = F'_{34},$$

$$F'_{13} = F_{13} \cos \theta - F_{14} \sin \theta, \quad F'_{14} = F_{13} \sin \theta + F_{14} \cos \theta,$$

$$F'_{23} = F_{23} \cos \theta - F_{24} \sin \theta, \quad F'_{24} = F_{23} \sin \theta + F_{24} \cos \theta.$$

Expressing here F_{ij} in terms of X, Y, Z, L, M, N according to formulas 4.72 and σ and τ according to 11.8, we obtain:

$$X' = X\sigma + M\tau, \qquad L' = L\sigma - Y\tau,$$

$$Y' = Y\sigma - L\tau, \qquad M' = M\sigma + X\tau,$$

$$Z' = Z, \qquad\qquad N' = N.$$

Exercise 8. Show that the expressions $I = X^2 + Y^2 + Z^2 - L^2 - M^2 - N^2$ and $J = XL + YM + ZN = 0$ are invariant under coordinate transformation.

Exercise 9. Show that if the two expressions in exercise 8 are not both zero there exists a system of coordinates in which $Y' = Z' = M' = N' = 0$.

12. Are the equations of physics invariant?

We return now to physics. In Chapter 1 we arrived at certain equations which we considered fundamental, namely the equation of continuity (3.5),

12.1 $$\partial_i \rho u_i = 0,$$

the two sets of Maxwell's equations (4.61) and (4.62),

12.2 $$\partial_i F_{jk} + \partial_j F_{ki} + \partial_k F_{ij} = 0,$$

12.3 $$\partial_j F_{ij} = \varepsilon u_i,$$

and the equations of motion (6.3),

12.4 $$\partial_j T_{ij} = 0 \qquad (i = 1, 2, 3),$$

with (compare 6.2, 5.1, 3.5)

12.5 $$T_{ij} = M_{ij} - E_{ij} = \rho u_i u_j - \delta_{ij} p - F_{ik} F_{kj} + \tfrac{1}{4} \delta_{ij} F_{sk} F_{ks}.$$

The fact that the indices run here from 1 to 4 (except in 12.4) suggested four-dimensional geometry, which we introduced in sections 7, 8, and 9. The fact that x_4 in the above equations is imaginary (compare 4.7) suggested the peculiarities discussed in section 11. Now that we have followed these suggestions and built a mathematical theory we have to see what results from its application. In addition to following these suggestions we have introduced into the theory a feature that was not directly called for by physics; namely, we made our theory independent of coordinates.

Returning to physics we have to ask ourselves again what we actually need for it, a *diagram* or a *geometry*. (See the discussion at the beginning of section 8, p. 32.) In other words, are the coordinate axes essential or can they be changed at will, or, again, do the equations of physics express properties independent of the coordinate axes— are they invariant, or not?

In order to answer this question let us first consider the formal structure of equations 12.1–12.5.   Here the fundamental dependent variables are two scalars ρ and p, a vector u_i, and an antisymmetric tensor F_{ij}.

The left-hand side of equation 12.1 may be described as a result of multiplying the scalar ρ by the vector u_i, differentiating the resulting vector ρu_i, and contracting the tensor so obtained.   Since the operations of multiplication, differentiation, and contraction have been shown to be invariant, the scalar $\partial_i \rho u_i$ is independent of the system of coordinates used.   Consequently if it is zero in one system of coordinates it is zero in all systems of coordinates.   The continuity equation expresses, therefore, a fact independent of the system of coordinates employed.

Analogous reasoning applied to equations 12.3 would show the invariant character of that system.   The question of invariance of the first system of Maxwell's equations can be treated most simply by using the concept of the dual of the tensor F_{ij} introduced in section 10 (p. 48).   In fact, if in the expression $\partial_1 F_{23} + \partial_2 F_{31} + \partial_3 F_{12}$ we replace the F's by the corresponding D's that expression becomes

$$\partial_1 D_{14} + \partial_2 D_{24} + \partial_3 D_{34} = \partial_i D_{i4}.$$

By similarly treating the other equations of the same set we can write them all

12.2′ $$\partial_i D_{ij} = 0.$$

The invariance of this follows from the same considerations as for sets 12.1 and 12.3.

Formula 12.5 contains only multiplications, contractions, and additions, so that there is no doubt concerning its invariance, but the situation changes when we come to set 12.4.   The vector $\partial_j T_{ij}$ has been obtained by invariant operations, but set 12.4 states only that three of its components are zero, a statement that obviously depends on the choice of coordinate axes and is *not invariant.*

We have now two courses open before us.   One is resignation; we can say that physics is *not* like geometry in this respect, and that we can use only four-dimensional notation, a four-dimensional diagram, but not four-dimensional geometry.   The other course is adventure: we may try to play the game of geometry.   Let us pretend that we can apply the formulas of transformation of coordinates in this case. We know that there will be a difference between the theory we obtain and the physics which we undertook to translate into our language, but it may be that the difference will amount numerically to very little.   Consider the fourth component of the vector $\partial_j T_{ij}$.   We found (compare remark following 6.3) that one of the terms of this expression, $\partial_j M_{4j}$, vanishes, and that the other, $\partial_j E_{4j}$, gives $Xu + Yv + Zw$, where u, v, w are the components of velocity.   However, in order to present the Maxwell equations in a simple form we had to choose our units in such a way that the velocity of light became unity.   Ordinary velocities are of the order of magnitude of one ten-millionth of the velocity of light, so we see that by setting the fourth component of the left-hand side of 12.4 equal to zero we would commit an error that is numerically very small.   This encourages us to go on with our adventure and to try to force the geometrical character on physics.   In order to do this let us go beyond the formal structure of our formulas and recall the meaning of our fundamental quantities.   The components u_i of the velocity vector were given (see 1.2, 4.9) as

$$12.8 \qquad u_1 = \frac{dx}{dt}, \qquad u_2 = \frac{dy}{dt}, \qquad u_3 = \frac{dz}{dt}, \qquad u_4 = i.$$

This identification is obviously not independent of the coordinate system, since it gives preference to the fourth coordinate.   We may suspect that this is the source of our difficulty and that this difficulty may be overcome if we find an invariant identification to take the place of that given by 12.8.   The next section will prepare the way for this.

13.   Curves in the new geometry

The root of the difficulty is that our description of motion was not invariant; motion was described by giving the dependence of the coordinates x, y, z on time.   Geometrically this means that, expressing three of our coordinates, x_1, x_2, x_3, as functions of the fourth, x_4, this fourth coordinate is given preference, a concept incompatible with the idea of invariance.

To clarify the situation let us consider analogous situations in lower dimensions.   In two dimensions, by giving one coordinate, y, as a function $f(x)$ of the other, we describe a plane curve; in three dimensions, giving two coordinates, y and z, as functions $f(x)$ and $g(x)$, we describe a space curve.   Thus we see that the description of motion of a particle using four-dimensional geometry is analogous to the description of curves in the plane and in space.   We shall therefore consider the motion of a particle as a curve in four-dimensional space or space-time.   (This idea may be also arrived at by noticing that motion of a particle in one dimension, e.g., up and down, may be represented by a diagram in which one axis is used to indicate time and the other to indicate the distance traveled.   Thus *one*-dimensional motion is represented by a *two*-dimensional diagram, and it is natural to expect three-dimensional motion to be represented in four dimensions.)

Giving preference in these descriptions to one coordinate is neither essential nor confusing.   We have an idea of a curve independently of the coordinate system, and we know that the coordinate x plays a special part only in the particular description, and that as far as the curve itself is concerned all coordinates play the same part (or may be dispensed with altogether).   In four dimensions the situation is not so favorable because the absence of four-dimensional intuition (or corresponding habits) makes it difficult to treat motion (or curves) without coordinates.   Since this is so we should try to treat all coordinates on the same footing, and as a preparation we will now give a description of curves in two and three dimensions in which all coordinates are on the same footing.   In the plane a straight line may be represented by

$$x = ap + b, \qquad y = cp + d;$$

a circle by

$$x = r \cos p, \qquad y = r \sin p;$$

in space a line by

$$x = ap + b, \qquad y = cp + d, \qquad z = ep + f;$$

a helix by

$$x = r \cos p, \qquad y = r \sin p, \qquad z = kp, \qquad \text{etc.}$$

In all these examples, to every value of the "parameter" p there corresponds a point of the curve.   In general, if we set

$$x = f(p), \qquad y = g(p), \qquad z = h(p),$$

we have what we call a parametric representation of a curve (compare parametric form of equation of straight line in 7.11).   In the same way a curve in four dimensions, which we interpret to mean the motion of a particle, may be represented by giving all the coordinates x_i as functions of a parameter p.

The defect of this method is that it contains a certain arbitrariness; we may substitute for p another parameter q by making p an arbitrary increasing function of q.   However, this arbitrariness, affording us a certain freedom of choice, may be turned to advantage in that by choosing the parameter in an appropriate fashion we may achieve some simplifications.   The usual way is to choose the arc length along the curve as the parameter.   Without going into detail we shall state that arc length between points corresponding to values p_1 and p of the parameter is given by

$$13.1 \qquad s = \int_{p_1}^{p} \sqrt{\left(\frac{dx}{dp}\right)^2 + \left(\frac{dy}{dp}\right)^2 + \left(\frac{dz}{dp}\right)^2} \, dp,$$

and that in the special case when s is used as parameter p we may differentiate both sides and obtain

$$13.2 \qquad \left(\frac{dx}{ds}\right)^2 + \left(\frac{dy}{ds}\right)^2 + \left(\frac{dz}{ds}\right)^2 = 1.$$

We may consider in general dx/dp, dy/dp, dz/dp as the components of a vector tangent to the curve. The change of parameter would multiply these derivatives by the same number, i.e., substitute another tangent vector for that one. The quantity

$$(dx/dp)^2 + (dy/dp)^2 + (dz/dp)^2$$

gives the square of the length of the tangent vector, and the above equality 13.2 expresses then the fact that, if we use arc length as the parameter, the length of the tangent vector whose components are the derivatives of the coordinates with respect to the parameter is unity.

We come thus to the idea of a unit tangent vector. It characterizes in every point the direction of the curve, and its components are the direction cosines of the tangent.

We may try to go through an analogous process for curves in four-dimensional space, which, as we saw, may be taken to represent motions. If we succeed, the vector at which we arrive will appear as a natural thing to identify with the vector of components u_i that appears in our formulas. Starting with any parametric representation $x_i = x_i(p)$, where p may be, for example, time, we try to change our parameter by introducing a new variable q, making p a function of q, and choosing this function in such a way that

$$\left(\frac{dx_1}{dq}\right)^2 + \left(\frac{dx_2}{dq}\right)^2 + \left(\frac{dx_3}{dq}\right)^2 + \left(\frac{dx_4}{dq}\right)^2 = 1.$$

But $dx_i/dq = (dx_i/dp) \cdot (dp/dq)$; so that the function $p(q)$ must be such that

$$\frac{dp}{dq} = \frac{1}{\sqrt{(dx_1/dp)^2 + (dx_2/dp)^2 + (dx_3/dp)^2 + (dx_4/dp)^2}}.$$

Is this possible? If the original p is time, the expression under the radical sign will be $u^2 + v^2 + w^2 - 1$; and for motions whose velocities are smaller than the velocity of light (section 4) this is negative, so that we would obtain an imaginary value for dp/dq. To avoid this unpleasantness let us standardize our parameter (this is in accordance with our definition of a unit vector as one whose square is ± 1) by requiring $(dx_i/dq) \cdot (dx_i/dq)$ to be -1 instead of 1. Then we find for dq/dp the expression $\sqrt{1 - (u^2 + v^2 + w^2)}$, and we may write

13.3 $$\frac{dx_1}{dq} = \frac{u}{\sqrt{1 - \beta^2}}, \qquad \frac{dx_2}{dq} = \frac{v}{\sqrt{1 - \beta^2}}, \qquad \frac{dx_3}{dq} = \frac{w}{\sqrt{1 - \beta^2}},$$

$$\frac{dx_4}{dq} = \frac{i}{\sqrt{1 - \beta^2}},$$

where β stands for $\sqrt{u^2 + v^2 + w^2}$, i.e., for what we call speed (the length of the velocity vector). These quantities we want to identify with the components of the vector u_i that appears in our formulas. Since, ordinarily, β is very small, the radical $\sqrt{1 - \beta^2}$ is very near to unity and our new identification differs *very little numerically* from our old identification (12.8). On the other hand, the new values for u_i are, according to their derivation, the components of a vector, so that if we adopt this identification and also agree to set the fourth component of the divergence of the tensor T_{ij} equal to zero we obtain an invariant theory whose statements differ only very slightly from those accepted in classical physics. It remains to be seen whether there are cases in which the discrepancy is large enough to be tested by experiment.

3

SPECIAL RELATIVITY

Guided by the view that the formulas of physics ought to be interpreted in four-dimensional geometry we were led to the interpretation of the motion of a particle as a curve in space-time. By analogy with a curve in ordinary space where arc length, s, is often used as a parameter, we introduced a standard parameter, which we may also call arc length and denote by s, for curves in space-time. The derivatives dx_i/ds of the coordinates of a point on the curve may be considered as the components of a vector tangent to the curve (the square of this vector is -1 in every point; we agreed to refer to such a vector as a unit vector also). We have then at every point x_1, x_2, x_3, x_4 of such a curve a unit vector dx_i/ds, and we agreed to identify this vector with the vector u_i that appears in our fundamental laws of physics (11.1–11.5), so that

$$u_i = \frac{dx_i}{ds}.$$

In this chapter we want to consider some consequences of this identification.

14. Equations of motion

The one thing that was not satisfactory about the formulas of physics was the fact that according to 12.4 only three components of the vector $\partial_i T_{ij}$ are equal to zero. In this section we shall see how this defect is corrected by our adoption of the new identification. But before we do that we have to study some immediate consequences of this identification.

Previously, a motion of a particle has been described by giving the position of the particle in different moments of time, i.e., the coordinates x, y, z as functions of t. Given these functions, we can calculate for every moment the velocity vector of the particle, a vector of components

$$u = \frac{dx}{dt}, \qquad v = \frac{dy}{dt}, \qquad w = \frac{dz}{dt}.$$

Now, the same motion is described by giving x_1, x_2, x_3, x_4 as functions of s, and we have a vector of components $u_i = dx_i/ds$ which, owing to the special choice of the parameter, satisfies the equation

14.1 $$u_1{}^2 + u_2{}^2 + u_3{}^2 + u_4{}^2 = -1.$$

Of course, we have merely two representations of the same thing. Given the $x_i(s)$, we can express s as a function of t from

$$x_4(s) = ti,$$

and, substituting the expression of s so found into $x_1(s)$, $x_2(s)$, $x_3(s)$, we will have x, y, z as functions of t. Or, given x, y, z as functions of t, we can arrive at the representation $x_i(s)$ as indicated in section 13.

Also, the space-time vector u_i and the space vector u, v, w describe the same thing. Formulas 13.3 show how to find the components u_i in terms of the velocity vector u, v, w, and it is easy to find the u, v, w in terms of components u_i. We have simply

$$u = \frac{dx}{dt} = \frac{dx/ds}{dt/ds} = i\,\frac{dx_1/ds}{dx_4/ds} = i\,\frac{u_1}{u_4},$$

and, in a similar fashion,

14.2 $$v = i\,\frac{u_2}{u_4}, \qquad w = i\,\frac{u_3}{u_4}.$$

Thus, we see that the vector u_i determines the velocity of motion, and we will term it the *four-dimensional velocity vector*. On the other hand, as a unit vector it characterizes the *direction* in four dimensions of the curve representing motion; its components u_i are analogous to the direction cosines of the tangent (compare section 7, between formulas 7.41 and 7.5).

However, a velocity vector does not characterize the motion of a particle completely, since it specifies the kinematical aspect of the motion only. We need, in addition, to know the mass of the particle, so that we can form the *momentum* vector (compare beginning of section 1) whose components are mu, mv, mw. By analogy we can form the expressions mu_i or ρu_i (depending on whether we use the discrete or the continuous picture of matter) and consider them as the components of the *four-dimensional momentum vector*. Using the formulas 13.3 its components are

$$14.3 \quad mu_1 = \frac{mu}{\sqrt{1 - \beta^2}}, \qquad mu_2 = \frac{mv}{\sqrt{1 - \beta^2}}, \qquad mu_3 = \frac{mw}{\sqrt{1 - \beta^2}},$$

$$mu_4 = \frac{mi}{\sqrt{1 - \beta^2}}.$$

These we may call the mathematical components of the momentum vector. Its "physical components" are

$$14.31 \quad a = \frac{mu}{\sqrt{1 - \beta^2}}, \qquad b = \frac{mv}{\sqrt{1 - \beta^2}}, \qquad c = \frac{mw}{\sqrt{1 - \beta^2}},$$

$$d = \frac{m}{\sqrt{1 - \beta^2}}.$$

REMARK. We use here the positive value of the square root; notice that this makes d positive.

We can obtain a relation between the momentum components and mass if we take the sum of the squares of the components 14.3 or 14.31 and use 14.1, viz.,

$$a^2 + b^2 + c^2 - d^2 = -m^2.$$

In words, the negative square of mass is the square of the momentum vector, so that mass is essentially given by the length of the momentum vector. Another advantage of the four-dimensional representation is that the four dynamical quantities of a particle which in classical physics are represented by three numbers of one kind, namely by three components of a vector, and one number of another kind, the mass, are here given more elegantly by four numbers of the same kind, namely by four components of a vector.

As stated many times before, numerically $1 - \beta^2$ is in most applications very close to unity, so that the first three components of the four-dimensional momentum vector are *approximately* equal to the components of the three-dimensional momentum vector, and the last (physical) component of the four-dimensional momentum vector is, to the first approximation, equal to mass.

Let us consider more in detail this fourth component of the momentum vector. As just mentioned, to the first approximation it is equal to the mass m. If we want a better approximation we can develop the last of 14.31 according to powers of β and keep only two terms, thus obtaining the approximate equality

14.4 $$d = \frac{m}{\sqrt{1 - \beta^2}} = m + \tfrac{1}{2}m\beta^2,$$

in which the correction represented by the second term is nothing but *kinetic energy*. Of course, if ordinary units are used, this term has to be written as

14.41 $$\tfrac{1}{2}m \frac{V^2}{c^2},$$

where c is the velocity of light, and V is the velocity of the particle measured in the same units (according to our agreement in section 4 before formulas 4.3, β is the ratio of velocity of the particle to that of light). It is better to say then that the correction is kinetic energy divided by the square of the velocity of light. Sometimes this fact is expressed by saying (neglecting the other terms, which *are* in the majority of cases exceedingly small) that when a body is in motion its mass is increased by its kinetic energy (divided by the square of the velocity of light).

This result is of interest because of the close relationship that is thus established between mass and energy, a relationship that plays a prominent part in present-day physics (and military science). If we denote the kinetic energy by E and the change in mass by Δm, the above formula may be written as $\Delta m = E/c^2$ or as

$$E = c^2 \, \Delta m.$$

This relation appears to apply not only to motion of a body, for which it has been derived here, but also to other phenomena. It was first stated by Einstein in a paper published in 1905 in the following words: "Die Masse eines Körpers ist ein Mass für dessen Energieinhalt; ändert sich die Energie um L, so ändert sich die Masse in demselben Sinne um L/9.20²⁰ wenn die Energie in Erg und die Masse in Grammen gemessen wird," and he adds: "Es ist nicht ausgeschlossen, dass bei Körpern, deren Energieinhalt in hohem Masse veränderlich ist (Z.B. bei Radiumsalzen), eine Prüfung der Theorie gelingen wird."

Sometimes the whole expression $m/\sqrt{1 - \beta^2}$ is referred to as energy of the particle. Mass, from this point of view, appears then as part of the energy: that part which the particle possesses even when it is at rest. In other words, mass appears as the rest-energy of the particle. We could also call $m/\sqrt{1 - \beta^2}$ generalized mass and say that mass changes as a result of motion (compare the end of this section).

We are ready now to discuss the equations of motion 12.4, or

14.5 $$\partial_i M_{ij} = \partial_i E_{ij}.$$

The left member may be written as

$$\partial_i(\rho u_i u_j) - \partial_i \delta_{ij} p = \partial_i(\rho u_i) \cdot u_j + \rho u_i \cdot \partial_i u_j - \partial_j p.$$

The first factor of the first term vanishes according to the continuity equation 12.1; the second term may be written, recalling the definition of u_i, as

$$\rho \cdot \partial_i u_j \cdot u_i = \rho \cdot \partial_i u_j \cdot \frac{dx_i}{ds} = \rho \frac{du_j}{ds};$$

and the right member of 14.5, according to our former calculation (section 6), is $\varepsilon F_{ji} u_i$, so that the equations of motion may be written

$$\rho \frac{du_i}{ds} - \partial_i p = \varepsilon F_{ij} u_j;$$

or, if we use the discrete picture, considering both mass and electric density to be concentrated in one point, denoting mass by m, electric charge by e (pressure does not appear in this case),

14.51 $$m \frac{du_i}{ds} = eF_{ij} \frac{dx_j}{ds}.$$

These are the equations we are going to discuss. In applying them to physics we give preference to time by writing

14.52 $$m \frac{du_i}{dt} = eF_{ij} \frac{dx_j}{dt}.$$

This spoils the invariant form but does not change the content of the statement because the transition from 14.51 to 14.52 is equivalent to multiplication by ds/dt.

Using 4.72 (or 6.1), the first three equations become

$$m \frac{du_1}{dt} = e(X + Nv - Mw),$$

14.53 $$m \frac{du_2}{dt} = e(Y + Lw - Nu),$$

$$m \frac{du_3}{dt} = e(Z + Mu - Lv).$$

Before we discuss the applicability of these equations to physics we want to write down the equation that is obtained when we give to the index i the value 4. The corresponding equation was not "true" before we adopted the new identification. We saw at the end of the first chapter that the left-hand side of that equation was zero and that the right-hand side represented a quantity which, in general, was not zero. The fact that this "fourth equation" did not hold was felt at the end of the first chapter to be an unpleasant defect. After we introduced four-dimensional geometry in Chapter 2 the same fact was recognized in section 12 as causing the lack of invariance of our theory, and it forced us to look for a modification of the theory. This resulted in the introduction of the new identification for u_i. Now that we have adopted this new identification we want to see how it affects the fourth equation. Making $i = 4$ in 14.52 and using the last of the formulas 6.1 we obtain

14.54 $$m \frac{du_4}{dt} = ie(Xu + Yv + Zw).$$

The left member is no longer zero because u_4 is not a constant, as it was before (since according to 14.3 it depends on the velocity). The situation is even better, in that this equation is a consequence of the other three. In fact, if we multiply the left member of the first of 14.53 by the quantity $-u_1/u_4$ and the right member by iu (which is equal to that quantity according to 14.2), use in the same way $-u_2/u_4 = iv$ for the second and $-u_3/u_4 = iw$ for the third, and add the results, we obtain on the right the right-hand member of 14.54 and on the left we obtain the product

$$\frac{m}{u_4} \left(-u_1 \frac{du_1}{dt} - u_2 \frac{du_2}{dt} - u_3 \frac{du_3}{dt} \right).$$

The second factor of this, as we recognize by differentiating 14.1, is equal to $u_4 \, du_4/dt$, and so we have derived 14.54 from 14.53. The fourth equation, moreover, now has a definite physical meaning: the left member may be said to represent the time rate of change of energy (since the variable part of mu_4 has been recognized as kinetic energy), and the right member was recognized before (section 6) as the rate at which the energy of the field (potential energy) is being expended in moving the body. *The difficulty with the fourth equation has thus been settled* in a most satisfactory fashion. However, the system as a whole, or the first three equations, have to be tested by experiment (the fourth, being a consequence of the first three, cannot be wrong if these three are "true").

Since

$$\frac{du_i}{dt} = \frac{d}{dt}\left(\frac{dx_i}{ds}\right) = \frac{d}{dt}\left(\frac{dt}{ds}\frac{dx_i}{dt}\right) = \frac{d}{dt}\left(\frac{1}{\sqrt{1 - \beta^2}}\frac{dx_i}{dt}\right),$$

we may write our equations as

$$\frac{d}{dt}\left(m' \cdot \frac{dx}{dt}\right) = e(X + Nv - Mw),$$

14.6 $$\frac{d}{dt}\left(m' \cdot \frac{dy}{dt}\right) = e(Y + Lw - Nu),$$

$$\frac{d}{dt}\left(m' \cdot \frac{dz}{dt}\right) = e(Z + Mu - Lv),$$

where

14.7 $$m' = \frac{m}{\sqrt{1 - \beta^2}}.$$

The right-hand members of these equations (as stated in section 6) are the components of the force exerted by the electromagnetic field on the particle. Comparing the left member with the classical expressions 1.11 we see, then, that the correction resulting from our identification is equivalent to the substitution of m' for m in the classical equations of motion. We may say that our theory predicts that motion will be governed by the old equations in which mass has been replaced by a corrected mass, the correction being the kinetic energy (divided by the square of the velocity of light). In the vast majority of cases the factor $1/\sqrt{1 - \beta^2}$ is very close to 1, but there are a few cases where it is not, and these cases afford an opportunity to test the new theory and to see whether it or the old one is better qualified to give an account of experimental results. Early experiments with "cathode-ray particles" by Bucherer seem to have verified the predictions of the new theory, and the result seems to have been confirmed since then several times. Formulas equivalent to 14.6 are now used in calculations involved in the construction of powerful cyclotrons.

15. Lorentz transformations

Now that we see that the new identification removes the difficulty in connection with the fourth equation of motion (and results in a modification of the theory acceptable from the experimental point of view) we want to consider some other consequences, and in the first place we want to give a discussion (promised in section 8) of the physical

significance of the transformation of coordinates. The new feature
of the situation compared with the old, where we used three-dimensional space and time separately, is the greater freedom of choice of
the reference system. From our present point of view we may describe
the old situation by saying that we could change freely from a set of
vectors **i, j, k** to another orthonormal set of three vectors perpendicular
to the same vector **l**. Now **l** is also subject to change. Instead of a
three-parameter group of rotations of the coordinate system we have
now at our disposal a six-parameter group given by formulas 11.4 and
11.5, with the restriction that **l** must go into a vector **l'** in the same
funnel of the cone. We want to see what this means physically.

In general, in one system of coordinates a geometrical configuration
is described by certain numbers (e.g., coordinates of its points) and
certain equations (e.g., equations of its straight lines); in another
system of coordinates the same configuration will be characterized by
other numbers and other equations, but it will be *another description
of the same configuration*, or, we may say, another identification which
is theoretically just as good as the first, but may be more, or less,
convenient for practical purposes. As was stated before, in geometry
we often make a choice of a coordinate system which is guided by the
properties of the object we are studying and our own position in space.
If we study an ellipsoid we choose, for coordinate axes, its principal
axes; or, in other circumstances, we choose the direction away from
us as the y axis, the direction to the right as the x axis, the vertical
direction as the z axis. In principle, all axes are permitted. The
same general situation obtains in physics, considered as four-dimensional geometry. We have many systems of coordinate axes at our
disposal, and we wish now to investigate what use we can make of
this arbitrariness, or how we can adjust the choice of axes to the
requirements of a given situation. In particular, we are interested
in the choice of the t axis.

The object we want to study in the first place is the motion of a
particle. We represented such a motion by a curve in four-space (and
a straight line we considered as a special case of a curve). At every
point of that curve we have a unit tangent vector, the four-dimensional
velocity vector of components a, b, c, d; or we may characterize it by
the three-dimensional velocity components u, v, w. If we pass to
another coordinate system the components a, b, c, d will be changed,
and so will the components u, v, w. If the coordinate transformation
affects only the space coordinates x, y, z then the component d will not
be affected, and therefore β will not change. In other words, u, v, w
will be changed but not $u^2 + v^2 + w^2$; the velocity vector will have

different components, but its absolute value, the speed, will be the same. This is essentially as in old physics; the new feature is in the *existence of transformations affecting t,* and the most striking result of it is expressed in the following theorem.

Theorem. For every motion it is possible at every moment to choose a system of space-time coordinates in such a way that the speed is zero.

Proof. We know that the unit tangent vectors to a curve representing a particle moving with a velocity less than the velocity of light are vectors of square -1. All we have to do is to choose as our 1 vector the unit tangent vector at the point corresponding to the given moment, and to choose as our **i, j, k** vectors any three vectors forming an orthonormal set with that **1**. In this system the components of the unit tangent vector will be the components of **1**, i.e., **0, 0, 0, 1,** and this means that the three-dimensional velocity is zero.

Because of the importance of this theorem it seems desirable to give another proof of it which has the advantage that, instead of showing the possibility of *choosing* a coordinate system for a motion given in the abstract, it shows how to *change* the coordinate system if the motion is given concretely with reference to a coordinate system. If the reader prefers the preceding proof it shows that he has already entered into the spirit of the subject.

Without changing the time axis, change the space axes so that the motion, at the moment considered, takes place along the z axis. We have then $a = b = 0$. Now consider a transformation involving z and t. Denoting the new components of the four-dimensional velocity vector by a', b', c', d', we have (11.32)

$$a' = 0, \qquad b' = 0, \qquad c' = c\sigma + d\tau, \qquad d' = c\tau + d\sigma.$$

If we want to make $c' = 0$ we have to choose the angle ψ so that

$$\frac{\tau}{\sigma} = \sin \psi = -\frac{c}{d}.$$

If c is in absolute value less than d, and this is so for all motions of bodies so far observed, an angle satisfying this relation, and therefore a system of coordinates for which $a = b = c = 0$, can be found. From formulas 14.31 it follows that in such a system $u = v = w = 0$, and the theorem is proved again.

The theorem just proved is often expressed by saying that *every particle can be transformed to rest.*

After we have found a coordinate system in which a particle is at rest we can perform any transformations of space coordinates and the property will not be destroyed. Any transformation involving time, on the contrary, will result in introducing non-zero space components of the velocity vector. We see, therefore, that whether a particle is at rest in a coordinate system depends exclusively on the choice of the time axis, so that the choice of the time axis is equivalent to the choice of a body which we desire to consider at rest. In other words, the direction of the time axis may be characterized by indicating what particle is at rest in the corresponding coordinate system.

What time axis we actually choose depends, as in geometry, on circumstances. Ordinarily we shall want to consider ourselves as being at rest, or our laboratory, or the earth.

In the preceding we spoke of a motion of a particle at a given moment. In general, in a given system of space-time coordinates a particle may be at rest at one moment and not at rest at some other time. But there exists a class of particles which, if transformed to rest for one moment, will be at rest always. This consists of those particles whose representative four-dimensional curves have the same tangent vector at all points, i.e., of straight lines. It is clear that, if the direction of such a straight line is taken as the direction of the t axis, the velocity in this coordinate system will be zero. But if we choose any other (cartesian) coordinate system, the three-dimensional velocity u, v, w will be constant in absolute value and direction, so that we will have a rectilinear uniform motion. From our point of view, then, the distinction between uniform rectilinear motion and rest is a non-essential one which does not exist until we introduce a four-dimensional coordinate system. It is of the same nature as the distinction between lines that are and those that are not parallel to the x axis in ordinary analytic geometry.

If a motion is not uniform and rectilinear then there is no coordinate system in which the particle is permanently at rest. But, rather than make a strict distinction between particles that are and those that are not in uniform rectilinear motion (or at rest), it is more in keeping with our point of view to speak of particles that may be (within experimental error) considered at rest for a sufficiently long period of time.

We are now in a position to explain the name and the origin of the theory we are studying. We saw that in this theory there is no such thing as absolute rest or absolute motion of a body. If it is at rest with respect to one system of coordinates it may move with respect to another, and vice versa; we can only speak of relative motion; that is where the name *relativity* comes from.

If we adopt this point of view, we have to consider as permissible all transformations of coordinates from one to any other cartesian coordinate system. Later on we shall consider other, more general, systems of coordinates, and therefore more general coordinate transformations. We shall replace our equations by more general ones which will be invariant under these more general coordinate transformations. In comparison with this situation we may say that we have been considering only special coordinate transformations and properties invariant under them; therefore the present theory is called "special relativity theory."

It may be mentioned that the historical order of appearance of the ideas of our subject, as so often happens, has been quite different from the order which seems natural and in which we have presented them. First the formulas of transformation involving space coordinates and time were introduced by Lorentz without, however, giving to them the meaning they now have. In Lorentz's theory there exists one universal time t, and other times t' play only an auxiliary part. The credit for taking the decisive step recognizing the fact that all these variables are on the same footing is due to Einstein (1905). The four-dimensional point of view, after some preliminary work had been done by Poincaré and Marcolongo, was introduced most emphatically by Minkowski in 1908.

16. Addition of velocities

As explained in section 14 we have two ways of characterizing the velocity of a body: by means of the three-dimensional velocity vector, and by means of the four-dimensional velocity vector. We can pass from one representation of velocity to the other without difficulty, and the two methods are equivalent as long as we do not change our coordinate system. But if we come to study the relative motion of one body with respect to another and want to define the relative velocity, the four-dimensional point of view leads to conceptions that are at variance with commonly accepted ideas, and we want to devote the present section to the clarification of this situation. It is natural to reduce the definition of relative velocity of a body with respect to another body to the conception of the velocity of a body in a coordinate system by saying: *By velocity of the body B with respect to a body A we mean the velocity of B in a system of coordinates in which the velocity of A is zero.*

If we want to find the velocity of B with respect to A we have to transform our coordinates so that in the transformed coordinate system A is at rest. It is clear that the meaning of relative velocity is made to depend, by the preceding definition, on what we mean by transformation of coordinates. If by transformation of coordinates we mean only transformation of three-dimensional coordinates—transition to moving axes—we have the old idea of relative velocity. If, on the other hand, we consider four-dimensional coordinate axes, and our transformation of coordinates involves the coordinate x_4, or t, in the sense of the theorem of section 15, it is clear that we give a new meaning to relative velocity, and we should not be surprised if the so-defined "relativistic" relative velocity will possess properties different from those of the "classical" relative velocity.

Assume that we have two systems of reference A and B, and that the relation between them is given by the formulas

16.1 $x_A = x_B, \quad y_A = y_B, \quad z_A = \sigma z_B + \tau t_B, \quad t_A = \tau z_B + \sigma t_B.$

If we consider a particle which is at rest with respect to B, i.e., a particle whose coordinates x_B, y_B, z_B have the same values for all t_B, viz., a, b, c respectively, we find from the above formulas, if we want to describe it in the A system, that

$$x_A = a, \quad y_A = b, \quad z_A = \frac{c}{\sigma} + \frac{\tau}{\sigma} t_A$$

(the last relation is obtained by eliminating t_B from the transformation formulas). This means that our particle moves with the velocity

16.2 $U = \dfrac{\tau}{\sigma}$

from the point of view of the A system. Solving the above transformation formulas for the B quantities, we will find formulas of the same form with the same σ but with τ replaced by $-\tau$. It follows that a point at rest with respect to the A system will be considered as moving with velocity $-U$ with respect to the B system. That is what one would expect.

Now consider a particle that moves in the B system with a constant velocity V in the positive sense along the z_B axis. Its motion will be described in the B system by

$$x_B = a, \quad y_B = b, \quad z_B = c + V t_B,$$

and in the A system by

$x_A = a, \quad y_A = b, \quad z_A = \sigma(c + V t_B) + \tau t_B, \quad t_A = \tau(c + V t_B) + \sigma t_B.$

Eliminating t_B, we obtain

$$z_A(\sigma + \tau V) = c + t_A(\sigma V + \tau)$$

or

$$z_A = \frac{c}{\sigma + \tau V} + \frac{\sigma V + \tau}{\sigma + \tau V} t_A.$$

In other words, the velocity of the particle, as described from the point of view of the A system, will be

$$W = \frac{\sigma V + \tau}{\sigma + \tau V},$$

or, dividing numerator and denominator by σ and using 16.2,

16.3 $$W = \frac{U + V}{1 + U \cdot V}.$$

This is the velocity of a particle in the A system which in the B system moves with the velocity V if the B system itself (i.e., a particle at rest in the B system) moves with the velocity U in A. Formula 16.3 is the Einstein formula for addition of velocities that applies when two motions are in the same direction. It should be compared with the formula of addition of classically defined relative velocities

16.4 $$W = U + V.$$

Of course, there is no contradiction between the two formulas, because they refer to different quantities. Still it is legitimate to ask which formula is better from the point of view of experiment; which, if any, is "correct" for the relative velocities that we actually measure.

In ordinary units the second term in the denominator in formula 16.3 should be divided by the square of the velocity of light, so that for moderate velocities the formulas give results that differ very little numerically, and it seems to be difficult to devise an experiment with high enough velocities of material particles so that the formulas could be tested directly. In the next section we shall consider what happens when one of the velocities is that of light. In the meantime we mention that formula 16.3 is a special case of a more general formula which applies when the two motions are not necessarily in the same directions.

17. Light corpuscles, or photons

In studying curves in four-space representing motions of particles we succeeded (section 13) in choosing a standard parameter, s, by considering the expression

$$\left(\frac{dx_1}{dp}\right)^2 + \left(\frac{dx_2}{dp}\right)^2 + \left(\frac{dx_3}{dp}\right)^2 + \left(\frac{dx_4}{dp}\right)^2$$

and by setting dp/ds equal to the reciprocal of the square root of minus the above expression. This procedure would not work if the above expression were equal to zero. We can imagine in our four-dimensional geometry curves and straight lines for which the above expression *is* zero (section 11), and the question arises: what will be the physical interpretation of such curves? In other words: is there anything in physics that could be identified with such curves in the same way that motions of particles are identified with curves for which the above expression is negative? In order to answer this question let us calculate the three-dimensional velocity corresponding to such a curve; if the above expression is zero for one choice of parameter it will be zero for all choices. Using time as parameter, and using physical coordinates, we have then

$$\left(\frac{dx}{dt}\right)^2 + \left(\frac{dy}{dt}\right)^2 + \left(\frac{dz}{dt}\right)^2 - 1 = 0,$$

or

$$u^2 + v^2 + w^2 = 1;$$

i.e., we can say that curves of zero-square-tangent-vectors correspond to what we have to call, from the three-dimensional point of view, particles moving with the velocity of light. This suggests the identification of such curves in some way with propagation of light.

Since the time of Newton and Huygens two theories of light have been vying for supremacy with variable success. According to one, the so-called corpuscular theory, light consists (like matter on the discrete theory) of particles which have been called "photons" (Wolfers, 1923). According to the other theory, light is a wave phenomenon or, more generally, a process in a continuous medium, a mechanical process before Maxwell, an electromagnetic process after. For our present purposes the point of view of the corpuscular theory seems to be more suitable. If we adopt it we can make the above statement more specific by saying that *we identify curves of zero-square-tangent-vectors with photons, or with motion of photons.*

In so adopting the corpuscular theory of light we do not mean to say that that theory of light is correct, and still less that the other theory—the electromagnetic theory—is wrong. We simply want to show that the identification just mentioned permits us to give account of certain optical phenomena, and it is enough to mention polarization in order to see that other phenomena are left out.

To begin with, we want to point out an advantage of the relativity theory over classical theory if we take the point of view of the corpuscular theory of light. In classical theory, material particles and corpuscles of light seem to differ only in that the velocity of matter is less than that of light corpuscles. This is merely a *quantitative* difference. In relativity we have entirely different *kinds* of curves, and there are other differences entirely of *qualitative* nature that are consequences of our identification. This is more in keeping with the nature of light compared to matter as we know it from observation and it seems to constitute a strong argument in favor of the adoption of the point of view of relativity in general, and of the identification we are discussing now in particular.

We want next to discuss what is usually referred to as constancy of the velocity of light. The reader may have noticed that, when we were calculating the three-dimensional velocity corresponding to curves or lines with zero-square-tangent-vectors, we did not specify in what coordinate system we wanted to calculate this three-dimensional velocity. As a matter of fact, the result shows that it is independent of the coordinate system; i.e., no matter what bodies we consider as being at rest, we arrive at the same value for the velocity of light: in our units, 1.

This seems surprising. It contradicts the commonly accepted ideas about addition of velocities. But we have been led to formula 16.3 for the addition of velocities, which differs from the usual formula, and we can show that the constancy of velocity of light is in agreement with that new formula. In fact, if we consider the case where C moves with the velocity of light (that is *1* in our units) with respect to B (i.e., $V = 1$), and substitute this value in 16.3, we find that W is also 1; that is, motion with velocity 1 in one system is motion with velocity 1 in another system.

This discussion, of course, proves nothing but the inner consistency of the theory. Another question is whether the constancy of velocity of light, i.e., independence of this velocity from the choice of the system which is considered at rest, is consistent with experiment. As a matter of fact, it appears that it is. The weight of experimental evidence seems to be for it. Historically, results of some experiments by Michelson and Morley performed in 1887 and pointing in the same direction played an important role in the creation of the theory of relativity.

Having considered thus the question of velocity of light we pass to the discussion of another consequence of our identification.

We decided in a general way to identify straight lines whose vectors are of zero square with light (or the motion of photons) in the same way that straight lines whose vectors are of negative square are identified with matter (or uniform rectilinear motion of material particles). But a straight line (in four dimensions) does not characterize the motion of the particle completely; it only gives the velocity of the motion, that is, it characterizes it only kinematically. For a complete dynamical characterization we had to introduce (section 14) the mass of the particle, and that led us to introduce the momentum vector, whose square we found to be $-m^2$. The complete characterization of a material particle consists, then, of a line with a vector (of negative square) on that line. In the same way we shall characterize the motion of a photon by a line with a vector of zero square on it. We have thus the same picture for a material particle and a photon. In both cases we have a line with a vector on it; only in the first it is a vector of negative square; in the second, of zero square. This difference corresponds to the difference in the speeds of the particles in the classical theory. But in the classical theory this is a purely quantitative difference, and here, as mentioned before, it leads to qualitative differences, some of which we are going to consider.

In the first place *a photon cannot be transformed to rest*. In fact, transforming a photon to rest would mean finding a coordinate system such that in it the time axis would have the direction of the photon. This would mean that the vector 0, 0, 0, 1 would have zero square, which is impossible.

Then there is this distinction: two material particles may differ in mass, that means in the squares of their momentum vectors, and this is an essential difference because the square of a vector is not affected by a transformation of coordinates; all photons, on the other hand, have vectors of the same square, namely zero. We shall prove that, as a consequence of this, two photons never differ essentially; that is, given two photons there always exist two systems of coordinates in which the descriptions of the two photons are the same. To begin with, we may choose the origins of the two coordinate systems on the respective straight lines; next we may consider the two lines in the respective z-t planes. The momentum vectors of the corresponding photons will have now in their respective coordinate systems the components 0, 0, c, d and 0, 0, C, D, and since both vectors are of zero square we have

$$c^2 = d^2, \quad C^2 = D^2;$$

by appropriately choosing the sense on the z axes we can reduce these conditions to

17.1 $$c = d, \quad C = D.$$

Now in the second system perform the transformation

$$z' = z\sigma + t\tau, \quad t' = z\tau + t\sigma,$$

which, applied to the second vector, gives by 17.1

17.2 $$C' = D' = C(\sigma + \tau).$$

But σ and τ are subject only to the condition that $\sigma^2 - \tau^2 = 1$, so that we can choose $\sigma + \tau$ arbitrarily; if we make the choice

17.3 $$\sigma + \tau = \frac{c}{C},$$

we have $C' = c$, and the statement is proved.

This theoretical conclusion, that *any two photons are not essentially different from each other*, must be checked against experience. At first sight it seems to contradict well-known facts. We know that light differs from case to case; it differs in intensity and color. To account for the difference in intensity we assume that every beam of light consists of many photons, so that intensity (for a given color) depends on the number of photons in the beam. To account for the difference in color we remark that experiments show that color actually depends on the state of motion of the observer. When an observer approaches a source of light, color seemingly changes (Doppler effect), and so the field is clear for our assertion. Now let us see how it works out.

Before we treat the situation from the point of view of the relativity theory we have to say a few words about how color appears in physics as a measurable quantity. From the point of view of the wave theory a certain measurable quantity ν, "frequency," which corresponds to color in the sense that different colors correspond to different frequencies, is attached to light. In the corpuscular theory photons are characterized by their energies, E, and the fundamental relation between frequency and energy is given by the formula

17.4 $$E = h\nu.$$

Here h is the so-called Planck's quantum constant, which, for us, appears simply as coefficient of proportionality in the relation between the values of two quantities that measure the same thing in different units, much in the same way as c, the velocity of light, appears in the formula connecting mass and energy (compare 14.41). Of the two quantities, E and ν, which can be used to measure color, E will be the more convenient for our purposes because we use the corpuscular theory of light.

The question now is: with what quantity in our theory are we going to identify E? In order to obtain a suggestion we notice that E is of the character of kinetic energy; it plays for light particles the same role that kinetic energy plays for material particles. In discussing material particles (section 14) we identified kinetic energy with the second term in the development

$$\frac{m}{\sqrt{1 - \beta^2}} = m + \tfrac{1}{2}m\beta^2 + \cdots$$

of the fourth component of the momentum vector. Among the other terms the third and the following are negligible for ordinary material particles, and the first is a constant, so that it plays no part in these considerations, in which only the differences in energy are important. Besides, the corresponding constant for light is zero. Thus everything leads us to compare E with the fourth component of the momentum vector of light, or photon. We arrive in this way at a *new identification;* namely, we identify the mathematical quantity "time component of the momentum vector of a photon" with the physical quantity E, which, except for a factor of proportionality, is frequency, and measures color. This identification makes color dependent on the coordinate system, but this dependence, as was said before, is to be expected, and our next question is whether the precise form of this dependence corresponds to experimental facts.

Suppose that E is the energy of a light corpuscle in one system of coordinates; what will it be in another? We have already calculated how the components of a zero square vector change under a transformation of coordinates involving time. Formula 17.3 (together with 17.1) shows that the ratio of the fourth components of the two vectors (and, according to our identification, this means the ratio of the energies or frequencies) is

$$\frac{\nu'}{\nu} = \sigma + \tau.$$

On the other hand, we saw before (16.2) that the relative velocity of two bodies which are at rest in the corresponding systems of coordinates is

$$V = \frac{\tau}{\sigma}.$$

This gives

$$\frac{1 + V}{1 - V} = \frac{\sigma + \tau}{\sigma - \tau}.$$

Now taking into account the identity $\sigma^2 - \tau^2 = 1$, we find

17.4 $$\frac{\nu'}{\nu} = \sigma + \tau = \sqrt{\frac{1 + V}{1 - V}}.$$

Let us try to calculate the predicted change of frequency on the classical (wave) theory. If we have a wave of frequency ν there are ν vibrations per unit of time, and, since the velocity is unity, there will be ν waves per unit of length. Now, if we move toward the source with a velocity V, we shall travel the distance V in a unit of time and we shall meet $V \cdot \nu$ additional vibrations, so that the number of vibrations our eye receives in a unit of time will be $(1 + V) \cdot \nu$, and this will be the frequency for the moving observer. The two theories give then the predictions

$$\sqrt{\frac{1 + V}{1 - V}} \quad \text{and} \quad 1 + V$$

for the change in frequency due to motion of the observer, and the difference between these two values is too small to be subjected to an experimental test. Within experimental error both seem to fit observations equally well.

18. Electricity and magnetism in special relativity

In the preceding sections of this chapter we have discussed some modifications that are brought about by the theory of relativity in kinematics, mechanics, and optics. There are other modifications that have attracted a great deal of popular attention, owing to their sensational and paradoxical nature. We only *mention* the so-called effects of motion on the shape of bodies, lengths, and measure of time, and the fact that in the theory of relativity the conception of simultaneity loses its absolute character so that two events that are to be considered simultaneous in one system of space-time coordinates need not be simultaneous in another. But we shall say a few words about electricity and magnetism. Even in the first chapter the components of the electric and the magnetic force vectors were combined into one tensor F_{ij}, so that electricity and magnetism seem to be treated as two aspects, or manifestations, of a higher entity. But as long as we limit ourselves to transformations of space coordinates the components of F_{ij} corresponding to electricity are transformed among themselves, and those corresponding to magnetism among themselves, so that their unification in one tensor F_{ij} may be considered artificial. However, when we introduce transformations of space-time coordinates (formulas 11.32) the situation changes radically; we found at the end of section 11 the following relations:

$$X' = \sigma X + \tau M, \qquad L' = \sigma L - \tau Y,$$

18.1 $$Y' = \sigma Y - \tau L, \qquad M' = \sigma M + \tau X,$$

$$Z' = Z, \qquad N' = N.$$

The interpretation of these formulas is that if the unprimed letters give the components of electric and magnetic force in one system the primed letters will give the components of electric and magnetic force in a system that moves with respect to the first with velocity $V = \tau/\sigma$.

These formulas show that the distinction between electric and magnetic forces is not an absolute distinction but depends on the coordinate system used. We might, for example, have in the old coordinate system a purely electric field, $L = M = N = 0$; in the new system the magnetic components will be different from zero, viz., $-\tau Y, \tau X$. What is the physical meaning of this? It means that a field may have electric effects on one body but electric and magnetic effects on a second body that moves with respect to the first. This theoretical conclusion is verified by experiment. The fact may be restated by saying that an electric charge in motion has magnetic effects; it may, e.g., deflect a magnetic needle. As an example, the magnetic field of a moving electron may be easily calculated. We start with an electron at rest. Its magnetic field is supposed to be zero; its electric field is supposed to be independent of time and symmetric with respect to the point. Under these conditions Maxwell's equations reduce, as can be seen easily, to Newton's equations, which, as we know (section 1), give the inverse square law for the electric forces. The field of an electron in motion can now be obtained by applying the above formulas.

We considered, above, light as the motion of photons, but it was stated that there exists an alternative view according to which light is considered an electromagnetic phenomenon. Instead of the motion of a photon along the z axis one considers sometimes a "plane wave," i.e., an electromagnetic field of the form

$$X = f(z - t), \qquad L = g(z - t),$$

$$Y = g(z - t), \qquad M = -f(z - t),$$

$$Z = 0 \qquad\qquad N = 0,$$

where f and g are periodic functions. We note that in a plane wave

$$X^2 + Y^2 + Z^2 = L^2 + M^2 + N^2$$

and

$$XL + YM + ZN = 0.$$

19. The complete tensor

In section 6 we combined eleven fundamental quantities ρ, u, v, w, p, X, Y, Z, L, M, N into a symmetric tensor of space-time T_{ij} which we called the complete tensor. It will be the purpose of this section to investigate how far the eleven quantities are determined by T_{ij}. Our task will be made very much easier if we exercise our right to choose coordinate systems best suited to the handling of this tensor.

The tensor T_{ij} was defined by 6.2 as the difference $M_{ij} - E_{ij}$, and at the start we shall treat each part separately.

The hydrodynamical tensor M_{ij} was introduced in section 3 as $\rho u_i u_j - \delta_{ij} p$. We still consider these expressions, but the u_i are now expressed in terms of u, v, w by formulas 13.3. We find it convenient to change our notation again and to introduce four real numbers a, b, c, d defined by

19.1 $a = \sqrt{\rho} \cdot u_1, \qquad b = \sqrt{\rho} \cdot u_2, \qquad c = \sqrt{\rho} \cdot u_3, \qquad d = \sqrt{\rho} \cdot \dfrac{u_4}{i},$

or

19.11 $a = \dfrac{u \sqrt{\rho}}{\sqrt{1 - \beta^2}}, \quad b = \dfrac{v \sqrt{\rho}}{\sqrt{1 - \beta^2}}, \quad c = \dfrac{w \sqrt{\rho}}{\sqrt{1 - \beta^2}},$

$$d = \dfrac{\sqrt{\rho}}{\sqrt{1 - \beta^2}}.$$

These quantities are intermediate between velocity components and momentum components, and they have the advantage that the tensor of matter has a simple expression in terms of them. On the other hand, if we know them, we can find u, v, w, and ρ, and vice versa. We now write out the array of the tensor of matter, omitting the pressure term, which we will re-introduce later. Since the elements below the diagonal are equal to those above, we will not write them. The array then is as follows:

$$a^2 \quad ab \quad ac \quad iad$$
$$b^2 \quad bc \quad ibd$$
$$c^2 \quad icd$$
$$-d^2$$

19.2

The electromagnetic array, according to 5.2, is

19.3
$$X^2+L^2-h \qquad XY+LM \qquad XZ+LN \qquad i(NY-MZ)$$
$$Y^2+M^2-h \qquad YZ+MN \qquad i(LZ-NX)$$
$$Z^2+N^2-h \qquad i(MX-LY)$$

with

19.31 $\qquad h = \frac{1}{2}(X^2 + Y^2 + Z^2 + L^2 + M^2 + N^2).$

We try to simplify these arrays as much as possible by choosing appropriate systems of coordinates. This will be done in several steps.

1. We can always choose the x-y plane in such a way that the electric and magnetic vectors will be in it (when these vectors have the same direction, we can choose any plane containing that direction). In such a system of coordinates

19.4 $\qquad Z = 0, \qquad N = 0,$

so that four elements of the array in the upper right-hand corner of 19.3 are zero.

2. By a rotation in the x-y plane we can always make

19.41 $\qquad XY + LM = 0;$

this follows from the remark on p. 42. Using this relation in the easily proved identity

$$(XY + LM)^2 + (LY - XM)^2 = (X^2 + L^2)(Y^2 + M^2),$$

and introducing the notations

19.5 $\qquad \xi^2 = X^2 + L^2, \quad \eta^2 = Y^2 + M^2,$

we obtain $MX - LY = \pm \xi\eta$, and, since the signs of ξ and η are still at our disposal, we can choose them in such a way that

19.51 $\qquad MX - LY = -\xi\eta.$

Changing, if necessary, the sense of the x axis, we can assume that $MX - LY$ is negative. With the notation 19.5 and because of 19.4

we have now $h = \frac{1}{2}(\xi^2 + \eta^2)$ and the electromagnetic array becomes

19.32
$$
\begin{matrix}
\dfrac{\xi^2 - \eta^2}{2} & 0 & 0 & 0 \\[2ex]
& \dfrac{\eta^2 - \xi^2}{2} & 0 & 0 \\[2ex]
& & -\dfrac{\xi^2 + \eta^2}{2} & -i\xi\eta \\[2ex]
& & & \dfrac{\xi^2 + \eta^2}{2}.
\end{matrix}
$$

3. Further simplification of this array can be achieved only by considering two special cases.

(a) If $\xi^2 = \eta^2$ we can assume that $\eta = \xi$ and we have

19.33
$$
\begin{matrix}
0 & 0 & 0 & 0 \\
& 0 & 0 & 0 \\
& & -\xi^2 & -i\xi^2 \\
& & & \xi^2.
\end{matrix}
$$

(b) If $\xi^2 \neq \eta^2$ and, let us say, $\xi^2 > \eta^2$, we perform a pseudo-rotation whose effect on the components of the electromagnetic tensor is given by 18.1. For η', which is what η becomes in the new coordinate system, we obtain

$$
\begin{aligned}
\eta'^2 = Y'^2 + M'^2 &= (\sigma Y - \tau L)^2 + (\sigma M + \tau X)^2 \\
&= \sigma^2\eta^2 - 2\sigma\tau(YL - MX) + \tau^2\xi^2,
\end{aligned}
$$

which, using 19.51, becomes

$$
\sigma^2\eta^2 - 2\sigma\tau\xi\eta + \tau^2\xi^2 = (\sigma\eta - \tau\xi)^2,
$$

so that by setting $\tau/\sigma = \eta/\xi$ we can make $\eta' = 0$. The array then becomes

19.34
$$
\begin{matrix}
\dfrac{\xi^2}{2} & 0 & 0 & 0 \\[2ex]
& -\dfrac{\xi^2}{2} & 0 & 0 \\[2ex]
& & -\dfrac{\xi^2}{2} & 0 \\[2ex]
& & & \dfrac{\xi^2}{2}
\end{matrix}
$$

4. We intend now to simplify the representation of the vector of matter. In each of the cases (a) and (b) we can change the coordinate system without changing the electromagnetic array but we have to use different transformations. In (a) we may consider the array as representing the tensor $-v_i v_j$, where $\mathbf{v} = (0, 0, \xi, i\xi)$. If we apply the transformation whose coefficients are

$$
\begin{array}{cccc}
1 & 0 & -\alpha & -i\alpha \\[1em]
0 & 1 & -\beta & -i\beta \\[1em]
\alpha & \beta & 1 - \dfrac{\alpha^2 + \beta^2}{2} & -i\,\dfrac{\alpha^2 + \beta^2}{2} \\[1em]
i\alpha & i\beta & -i\,\dfrac{\alpha^2 + \beta^2}{2} & 1 + \dfrac{\alpha^2 + \beta^2}{2}
\end{array}
$$

(compare exercise 5 of section 11), which satisfies the restrictions 11.51 and may therefore be used to transform coordinates, we see that the $\mathbf{v}$ and therefore the array 19.34 is transformed into itself for any α and β. On the other hand, if we set $\alpha = \dfrac{a}{c - d}$, $\beta = \dfrac{b}{c - d}$, where a, b, c, d are the components of the vector of matter defined by 19.1, we find that the first two of the transformed components are:

$$
a' = 1 \cdot a - \frac{a}{c - d} \cdot c - \frac{ia}{c - d} \cdot id = a - \frac{a}{c - d}(c - d) = 0,
$$

$$
b' = 1 \cdot b - \frac{b}{c - d} \cdot c - \frac{ib}{c - d} \cdot id = 0.
$$

Our transformation does not affect the electromagnetic array, and it reduces the first two components of the vector of matter to zero.

5. In (b) we can achieve the same result: by a rotation in y-z plane we can reduce the y component of the vector of matter to zero; and by a pseudo-rotation in the x-t plane, the x component.

We can assume therefore that in both (a) and (b) the vector of matter is of the form $0, 0, c, d$ and the array of matter will be (compare 19.2)

19.35

$$
\begin{array}{cccc}
0 & 0 & 0 & 0 \\[0.5em]
 & 0 & 0 & 0 \\[0.5em]
 & & c^2 & icd \\[0.5em]
 & & & -d^2
\end{array}
$$

6. Although we achieved simplifications of the electromagnetic array by considering two special cases, now that we have used the simplified forms to obtain the reduction of the vector of matter to the form 0, 0, c, d we return to the form 19.32 of the electromagnetic array, which, although not as simple as 19.33 and 19.34, applies in all cases. Combining it with the array of matter 19.35 we obtain for $M_{ij} - E_{ij}$ (we still disregard pressure)

$$
\begin{array}{cccc}
\dfrac{\eta^2 - \xi^2}{2} & 0 & 0 & 0 \\[2ex]
 & \dfrac{\xi^2 - \eta^2}{2} & 0 & 0 \\[2ex]
 & & \dfrac{\xi^2 + \eta^2}{2} + c^2 & icd + i\xi\eta \\[2ex]
 & & & -\dfrac{\xi^2 + \eta^2}{2} - d^2.
\end{array}
$$

We shall try to bring this to diagonal form by a further change of the coordinate system, more precisely by a pseudo-rotation in the z-t plane. We have here (compare with the passage leading to 11.6)

$$
A = \frac{\xi^2 + \eta^2}{2} + c^2, \quad B = cd + \xi\eta, \quad C = \frac{\xi^2 + \eta^2}{2} + d^2.
$$

The possibility of diagonalization depends on the positiveness of Δ, which here is

$$
(\xi^2 + \eta^2 + c^2 + d^2 + 2cd + 2\xi\eta)(\xi^2 + \eta^2 + c^2 + d^2 - 2cd - 2\xi\eta)
$$
$$
= [(\xi + \eta)^2 + (c + d)^2][(\xi - \eta)^2 + (c - d)^2].
$$

Now we must distinguish two cases: (1) When $\xi = \pm\eta$ and $c = \pm d$ the quantity Δ is zero and diagonalization is not possible. We will refer to this case as the *singular case*. The array takes the form:

19.36
$$
\begin{array}{cccc}
0 & 0 & 0 & 0 \\[1ex]
 & 0 & 0 & 0 \\[1ex]
 & & \xi^2 + d^2 & i(\xi^2 + d^2) \\[1ex]
 & & & -(\xi^2 + d^2).
\end{array}
$$

(2) When $\Delta > 0$ and diagonalization by a pseudo-rotation in the z-t plane *is* possible. Since such a pseudo-rotation does not destroy the

form of either 19.32 or 19.35 we now have

19.37
$$\begin{matrix} \dfrac{\eta^2 - \xi^2}{2} & 0 & 0 & 0 \\[2mm] & \dfrac{\xi^2 - \eta^2}{2} & 0 & 0 \\[2mm] & & \dfrac{\xi^2 + \eta^2}{2} + c^2 & 0 \\[2mm] & & & -\dfrac{\xi^2 + \eta^2}{2} - d^2, \end{matrix}$$

with

19.38 $$\xi\eta + cd = 0.$$

Before we go on we formulate our results as

THEOREM 1.   By suitable choice of coordinate system the complete tensor (omitting pressure) can always be brought into one or the other of the forms 19.36 or 19.37.

Assume now that we are given a tensor with a diagonal array, and we want to know whether it can be interpreted as a complete tensor. If we denote the diagonal components by λ, μ, ν, and ρ and take into account the pressure p which has so far been left out (because it is not affected by any transformation of coordinates), the relations that must be satisfied will be written as follows:

$$\frac{\eta^2 - \xi^2}{2} - p = \lambda, \quad \frac{\xi^2 - \eta^2}{2} - p = \mu, \quad \frac{\xi^2 + \eta^2}{2} + c^2 - p = \nu,$$

$$-\frac{\xi^2 + \eta^2}{2} - p - d^2 = \rho, \quad \xi\eta + cd = 0.$$

Adding and subtracting the first two of these equations we have:

19.39 $$p = -\frac{\lambda + \mu}{2}$$

and

$$\eta^2 - \xi^2 = \lambda - \mu.$$

Adding and subtracting the next two we have:

19.6 $c^2 - d^2 = \nu + \rho - \lambda - \mu$ and $\xi^2 + \eta^2 + c^2 + d^2 = \nu - \rho,$

and from 19.38 we have

$$\xi^2\eta^2 = c^2 d^2.$$

These equations are easily solved, and they give

$$19.61 \quad \xi^2 = \frac{(\nu - \lambda)(\mu - \rho)}{\nu - \rho}, \quad \eta^2 = \frac{(\nu - \mu)(\lambda - \rho)}{\nu - \rho},$$

$$c^2 = \frac{(\nu - \mu)(\nu - \lambda)}{\nu - \rho}, \quad d^2 = \frac{(\lambda - \rho)(\mu - \rho)}{\nu - \rho}.$$

We see thus that, when the diagonal tensor is given, pressure is determined and the vector of matter is determined, since $a = 0, b = 0$, and the values of c and d are given by formulas 19.61. As far as the signs are concerned, the sign of d is always positive (compare Remark after 14.31) and the sign of c depends on the choice of sense on the z axis. This is arbitrary since the diagonal form of the given tensor is not affected by the change of sense of the axes. We can say then

THEOREM 2. In the diagonal case the vector of matter is determined by the complete tensor.

The electromagnetic stress-energy tensor is also determined by the complete tensor since ξ^2 and η^2 are given by formulas 19.61 and the non-zero components of the stress-energy tensor are expressed in terms of ξ^2 and η^2.

The components X, Y, Z, L, M, N of the electric and magnetic vectors satisfy the relations

$$X^2 + L^2 = \xi^2, \qquad Y^2 + M^2 = \eta^2, \qquad XY + LM = 0,$$

whence

$$X = \xi \cos \phi, \qquad L = \xi \sin \phi,$$

$$Y = -\eta \sin \phi, \qquad M = \eta \cos \phi,$$

where ϕ is *arbitrary*, and in the coordinate system we are using

$$Z = 0, \qquad N = 0.$$

The electric and magnetic components (in contradistinction to the components of matter and of the electromagnetic stress-energy tensor) are thus not entirely determined by the complete tensor (compare exercises 1 and 2 of section 5).

REMARK. We consider here the situation at one point of space-time only. The fact that the electric and magnetic vectors are not determined by the values of the components of the stress-energy tensor *at that point* does not mean that the electric and magnetic *fields* are not determined by the stress-energy *field*. The complete determination of the electric and magnetic field requires the consideration of the differential equations to which the fields are subjected and will not be discussed here.

We summarize the results concerning electric and magnetic quantities in the following two theorems:

THEOREM 3. In the diagonal case the complete tensor is split in a unique way into the tensor of matter and the electromagnetic stress-energy tensor.

THEOREM 4. The electric and magnetic force vectors are determined by the stress-energy tensor at that point up to an arbitrary angular constant.

We may ask ourselves now whether any given diagonal tensor may be interpreted as a complete tensor. In order to answer this question we note that since the left members of formulas 19.61 are squares the right members must be positive. Forming the expressions for $\xi^2 + c^2$, $\eta^2 + c^2$, $\xi^2 + d^2$, and $\eta^2 + d^2$, we find that the following inequalities must hold

$$19.71 \qquad \nu \geq \lambda, \quad \nu \geq \mu, \quad \mu \geq \rho, \quad \lambda \geq \rho,$$

so that all factors in the numerators of formulas 19.61 are non-negative. Since the denominator cannot be zero we must also have

$$19.72 \qquad \nu > \rho.$$

If these inequalities are satisfied the vector of matter and the electric and magnetic components as well as pressure can be found. However, since the vector of matter must be of negative square, or—if we consider a photon as matter—non-positive square, we must have $c^2 - d^2 \leq 0$, which, in terms of λ, μ, ν, ρ, is (compare 19.6)

$$19.73 \qquad \lambda + \mu \geq \nu + \rho.$$

We have thus

THEOREM 5. Necessary and sufficient conditions for a diagonal tensor to be interpretable as a complete tensor are given by the inequalities 19.71, 19.72, and 19.73.

We come now to the discussion of the case when $\Delta = 0$ and the tensor cannot be diagonalized. The array has then the form 19.36, which may be written as

$$\begin{matrix} 0 & 0 & 0 & 0 \\ & 0 & 0 & 0 \\ & & k^2 & ik^2 \\ & & & -k^2. \end{matrix}$$

If such an array is given we have equations

$$\xi^2 + d^2 = k^2, \qquad \eta^2 = \xi^2, \qquad c^2 = d^2$$

for the determination of the matter and electric components.

It is clear that in this case the splitting of the complete tensor into matter and electric part is not unique. We could, for example, make $\xi = k$, $d = 0$, so that there could be an electric tensor but the tensor of matter would be zero; or we could make $\xi = 0$, $d = k$, so that the electromagnetic quantities would be zero but there would be a tensor of matter. We can, of course, have intermediate situations. In general, we set

$$\xi^2 = \eta^2 = k^2 \cos^2 \theta, \qquad c^2 = d^2 = k^2 \sin^2 \theta.$$

We have

THEOREM 6. In the singular case the splitting of the complete tensor into a tensor of matter and electromagnetic stress-energy tensor is not unique; in particular, we may interpret the complete tensor as representing matter only, or electromagnetism only.

REMARK. It is interesting and perhaps important to note that in the singular case the vector of matter is of zero square and represents light according to section 17. As far as the electromagnetic quantities are concerned, here $\xi^2 = \eta^2$, that is, according to 19.5, $X^2 + L^2 = Y^2 + M^2$, and also, according to 19.41, $XY + LM = 0$. These two relations imply

19.6 $$X = M, \qquad Y = -L$$

(or $X = -M$, $Y = L$, but this can be reduced to $X = M$, $Y = -L$ by changing the sense of the y axis). In other words, the electric and magnetic vectors are in the same relation as in a plane wave (see end of section 18). Thus, although in the singular case the complete tensor may be interpreted either as matter or as electromagnetic, the physical phenomenon is the same, namely light, in both interpretations.

The results of this section were obtained in a somewhat different way by E. Williams in a doctoral dissertation at the University of Michigan in 1946.

The importance of these results will become more apparent after we discuss the role that the complete tensor plays in general relativity (Chapter 5). Anticipating these developments we can say that the results of this section seem to show that curved space-time determines not only gravitational but also electromagnetic forces.

4

CURVED SPACE

The theory that has been developed so far consists of two parts: a general geometrical and a special physical one. The first, in addition to material analogous to that treated in ordinary geometry, includes general rules of operations on tensors; the second discusses definite tensor fields, namely two scalar fields, ρ and p, a vector field u_i, and a skew-symmetric field F_{ij}, as well as the special conditions imposed on these fields (viz., equations 12.1 and 12.5). Moreover, the physical part is independent of the geometrical part in that different physics could have been constructed; that is, different tensors or other differential equations could have been introduced.

In contrast to older theories, however, our new geometry contains a discussion of time—and we saw that there are some advantages to this change. The question now arises: is it not possible to extend this process of geometrization of physics so as to include physical phenomena in a properly modified geometry? Since physical quantities are given by tensors, this is equivalent to asking whether the geometry can be modified in such a way as to furnish the required tensors. The old three-dimensional geometry is entirely structureless—it is the same in every point. As Leibnitz put it: "every statement about a point applies in geometry to every other point." Moreover, it is the same in every direction, unlike the four-dimensional space-time in which at every point there are three types of directions (those of zero square and those of positive and negative squares). Thus four-dimensional space-time is no longer isotropic, and this anisotropy accounts in a way for the existence of (or for the distinction between) matter and light. But space-time *is* homogeneous in common with the old three-space; specifically, it is the same in all points and at all times. In other words, space-time possesses some structure as far as directions are concerned but it is structureless as far as position is

concerned.   Of course, this space-time which is the same at all points
(and at all times) cannot be used to explain the variety and change of
the outside world.   Could we not imagine a space-time with a more
radical structure which would do that?   We already know something
about what this structure would be if it could exist: it would furnish,
or manifest itself in, a tensor at every point, or in a tensor field.

The following considerations indicate where such a structure might
be found.

We began our discussion by considering gravitational motion.   Since
then we have traveled quite a distance and we have achieved some
results but we seem to have forgotten about gravitational motion.
The laws we have considered for "motion under gravitation" do not
have the property of invariance under Lorentz transformations which
we have found to hold (or which we have succeeded in imposing) for
other phenomena.   In the first place the gravitational force is a three-
dimensional vector for which we have not found a four-dimensional
interpretation, in contrast to the three-dimensional electric and magnetic vectors.   These, we recall, were successfully combined into the
four-dimensional tensor F_{ij}.   Then again since equations 1.50–1.52
involve derivatives with respect to the space coordinates and no time
derivatives it is obvious that they cannot be invariant under the
Lorentz transformations.   It appears therefore that our task is not
completed.   It would seem desirable to determine some four-dimensional configurations and four-dimensional equations which, on the
one hand, would possess the desired invariance properties and, on the
other, would furnish numerical results not too different from those
given by the classical gravitational theory.

We have now discussed two defects of the special relativity theory:
namely, the fact that space-time lacks structure and thus fails to connect physics with geometry organically; and the fact that it fails to
contain an invariant treatment of gravitational phenomena.   We shall
see that these two defects are connected; that they are, so to say, two
sides of the same situation.   More precisely, both can be remedied
by the same modification.

Let us begin the discussion leading to this modification by analyzing
gravitational motion more closely.   The force which acts on a particle
in a gravitational field depends (in addition to depending on the masses
producing the field) on the mass of that particle.   It is proportional
to that mass, so that in 1.3 we can write $c = -mM$, where M is a
positive quantity which depends on the field only.   If we compare
this with 1.11 and take into account 1.12 we find that we can write
the gravitational equation of motion as

$$\frac{du}{dt} + \frac{Mx}{r^3} = 0, \text{ etc.}$$

Since the *mass of the moving particle does not appear in these equations*, it follows that all particles with the same initial conditions move in the same way in a gravitational field.

Now, four-dimensionally, a motion of a particle is represented by a curve in space-time. In particular, in the absence of force it is a straight line in four-space. Three-dimensionally, force causes the motion to deviate from uniformity or rectilinearity or both; four-dimensionally, both deviations are deviations from rectilinearity. Thus if we want to describe four-dimensionally what is usually described as the effect of force on a moving particle we must speak of the deviation of a curve from a straight line in space-time, i.e., of the *curvature* of the line representing motion. Instead of saying that in a certain portion of space at certain times there are forces acting on particles, we must say, four-dimensionally, that in certain portions of space-time all curves representing motions of particles are curved, and that these curvatures, if we disregard electromagnetic phenomena, are independent of the nature of the particles. It is therefore natural to try to find the "cause" of that curvature in those portions of space-time where it occurs—we say that the lines representing motion are curved because space-time itself is curved. The idea of curved space-time is, of course, vague at this stage, in that it is only a suggestion. To make it somewhat more precise let us compare the *structureless* space-time to a *plane* surface. Tentatively, then we would expect that the *modified* space-time would be like a *curved* surface.

In order to be more precise we must therefore study curved surfaces and attempt, first of all, to determine whether a curved surface, that is the curvature of a surface, is connected with a tensor.

In the next section it will be shown that this is so, and in the following sections spaces of higher dimensions will be studied from this point of view.

The plan will be to begin with the simplest case, a case that is even simpler than that of a surface, viz., with a curve, and then to generalize step by step.

20. Curvature of curves and surfaces

Consider a curve in the plane. Assume that it possesses a tangent at every point; assume, further, that if the origin of coordinates is chosen at any point of the curve, and the tangent at the origin is chosen as the x axis, the curve in the neighborhood of the origin may be represented by a function

$$y = f(x),$$

which can be expanded into a power series converging in the neighborhood of the origin. The constant term of this expansion vanishes because the curve passes through the origin. The coefficient of the first power of x also vanishes, since the slope of the tangent, which is the x axis, must be zero. If we write the next term in the form

20.1 $\frac{1}{2}a_2x^2,$

the coefficient a_2 is called the *curvature* of the curve at the point considered, i.e., the point chosen for the origin. Since any point can be chosen for the origin this assigns a curvature to every point of the curve.

Next, consider a surface. Assume that it has a tangent plane at every point. Taking a particular point on the surface as the origin and the tangent plane at that point as the x-y plane, the surface may be represented by an equation $z = f(x, y)$. Again assume that for every point on the surface this function may be developed into a power series. The constant term and the coefficients of the first powers of the variables will vanish as before. The next group of terms, those that are quadratic in the variables, take the form

20.2 $z = \frac{1}{2}(a_{11}x_1{}^2 + 2a_{12}x_1x_2 + a_{22}x_2{}^2),$

where we use x_1 for x, and x_2 for y.

We may consider the coordinates x_1, x_2 as the components of a vector in the tangent plane which joins the origin to the projection of the point on the surface whose coordinates are x_1, x_2, $z = f(x_1, x_2)$. Thus the expression 20.2 assigns to every vector in the tangent plane a number (which may be considered the ordinate of a paraboloid approximating the surface). This assignment is independent of the coordinate system; i.e., if we choose another system of coordinates we shall have the same number assigned to the same vector although its components will have changed. In fact, in a rotation of the coordinate axes the degree of a polynomial is not affected so that the group of second-degree terms in the expansion of z is transformed into the group of second-degree terms of that expansion in the new coordinates. This is then a function whose values are numbers and whose argument is a vector; is it a tensor? Of course not, since it is not linear; but it is easy to introduce a tensor with which the function 20.2 is closely connected. Simply write, as in 10.1,

20.3 $a_{11}x_1y_1 + a_{12}x_1y_2 + a_{21}x_2y_1 + a_{22}x_2y_2 = s(\mathbf{x}, \mathbf{y}),$

using the coefficients a_{11}, a_{22} of the function 20.2 and in the third term replacing $2a_{12}$ by $a_{12} + a_{21}$ for the sake of symmetry. This is a (symmetric) tensor of the second rank, which depends on two vector arguments x and y, and from which the function 20.2 is obtained by setting the vector arguments equal to each other. Thus, in the case of a surface we have determined a tensor of rank two which expresses the curvature properties, i.e., the structure of the surface in so far as it describes its deviation from its tangent plane in the neighborhood of the point of contact. This encourages us in our enterprise: if we succeed in generalizing this result to higher dimensions, we may try to identify the generalization of this symmetric tensor of rank two with the symmetric tensor of rank two which, as we saw, combines in itself matter and electricity.

While ultimately we shall be successful in this enterprise, everything will not run altogether smoothly and some effort will be necessary in order to arrive at a tensor of rank two in the general case. The expressions that will present themselves immediately will not be exactly tensors, and even after a tensor has been obtained from them it will not be a tensor of rank two. In order to overcome these obstacles it will be necessary to make a more detailed study of ordinary surfaces before more complicated situations can be discussed.

The curvature of a curve is, so to say, an entirely external affair. From an intrinsic point of view (i.e., from the point of view of measurements which may be performed on the curve itself), the curve, no matter what its curvature, has the same properties as a straight line. When we speak of the curvature of the curve we speak of the relation of the curve to the plane (or space) surrounding it. The situation is not quite the same when we deal with surfaces. It is true that by measurements performed on some surfaces, as for example on a cylindrical surface, we cannot find any difference between them and a plane, but if we come to a surface of a sphere the situation changes. For example, the ratio of the circumference of a circle to its radius measured on the surface (i.e., the length of the arc of a great circle joining the center of the circle on the sphere to a point of the circumference) is less than 2π. In general, properties of surfaces are of two types: those that express the shape of the surface with respect to the imbedding space—they are called *external* properties; and those called *internal* properties, which can be expressed in terms of measurements performed on the surface. The tensor that we have introduced represents a mixture of both external and internal properties. Now there exists one combination of the components (compare 10.51), namely,

20.4
$$K = \begin{vmatrix} a_{11} & a_{12} \\ a_{21} & a_{22} \end{vmatrix},$$

which is called *total* or *Gaussian* curvature and which, as was discovered by Gauss, expresses an internal property—in that its value can be found from measurements performed on the surface itself. It is also an invariant in that its value is independent of the coordinate system used. The fact that K is an invariant is easily proved by replacing the a_{ij} by the corresponding coefficients a_{ij} of the same tensor in a different system of coordinates (see formulas 10.21). The proof that K expresses an internal property is much more difficult. It will be proved later in section 27 as a special case of a general proposition.

Since K is independent of the particular system of coordinates which was used to introduce the tensor a_{ij} it must be possible to express it without using *any* system of coordinates at all.

Above, the vector notation $s(\mathbf{x}, \mathbf{y})$ was used for the tensor 20.3; it will now be shown that the expression

20.5
$$\begin{vmatrix} s(\mathbf{x}, \mathbf{u}) & s(\mathbf{x}, \mathbf{v}) \\ s(\mathbf{y}, \mathbf{u}) & s(\mathbf{y}, \mathbf{v}) \end{vmatrix} = \begin{vmatrix} a_{ik}x_i u_k & a_{is}x_i v_s \\ a_{jk}y_j u_k & a_{js}y_j v_s \end{vmatrix},$$

where $\mathbf{x}, \mathbf{y}, \mathbf{u}, \mathbf{v}$ are arbitrary vectors, is equal to

20.6
$$K \cdot \begin{vmatrix} \mathbf{x \cdot u} & \mathbf{x \cdot v} \\ \mathbf{y \cdot u} & \mathbf{y \cdot v} \end{vmatrix} = K \cdot \begin{vmatrix} x_i u_i & x_i v_i \\ y_j u_j & y_j v_j \end{vmatrix}.$$

To prove this, consider the expression

$$\begin{vmatrix} a_{11} & a_{12} \\ a_{21} & a_{22} \end{vmatrix} \cdot \begin{vmatrix} x_1 & x_2 \\ y_1 & y_2 \end{vmatrix} \cdot \begin{vmatrix} u_1 & u_2 \\ v_2 & v_2 \end{vmatrix}.$$

By applying the law of multiplication of determinants to the second and the third factors and writing K for the first, 20.6 is obtained. Similarly, applying the law of multiplication of determinants first to the first two factors, then to the resulting determinant and the third factor, 20.5 results. Thus

20.7
$$\begin{vmatrix} s(\mathbf{x}, \mathbf{u}) & s(\mathbf{x}, \mathbf{v}) \\ s(\mathbf{y}, \mathbf{u}) & s(\mathbf{y}, \mathbf{v}) \end{vmatrix} = K \cdot \begin{vmatrix} \mathbf{x \cdot u} & \mathbf{x \cdot v} \\ \mathbf{y \cdot u} & \mathbf{y \cdot v} \end{vmatrix}.$$

An expression for K free of any system of coordinates can now be obtained by dividing the left-hand side by the second factor on the right. The vectors $\mathbf{x}, \mathbf{y}, \mathbf{u}, \mathbf{v}$ may be any arbitrary four vectors provided that the second factor on the right does not vanish. Setting $\mathbf{x} = \mathbf{i}$, $\mathbf{u} = \mathbf{i}$, $\mathbf{y} = \mathbf{j}$, $\mathbf{v} = \mathbf{j}$, where $\mathbf{i}, \mathbf{j}$ are two coordinate vectors, formula 20.4 results, and it is easily seen to hold for any system of coordinate vectors, which incidentally yields a new proof of the invariance of K.

Before leaving the topic of ordinary surfaces we want to establish a relation between curvature of surfaces and curvature of curves. The points common to our surface and the x-z plane constitute a plane curve whose equation in the x-z plane may be obtained from $z = f(x, y)$ by setting $y = 0$. It is clear that the x axis is a tangent to this curve and that the first term of the expansion of z as a function $f(x, 0)$ into a power series will be obtained by setting $x_2 = 0$ in 20.2. Thus

20.11 $$\tfrac{1}{2}a_{11}x_1{}^2$$

is the first non-vanishing term, so that comparison with 20.1 shows that the curvature of the curve is a_{11}, or by 20.3 the value $s(\mathbf{i}, \mathbf{i})$. Since any plane passing through the z axis can be considered the x-z plane, or any unit vector in the tangent plane can be considered the coordinate vector $\mathbf{i}$, we have established the result that the curvature at the point of contact of a curve, resulting from the intersection of the surface with a normal plane, is $s(\mathbf{i}, \mathbf{i})$, if $\mathbf{i}$ is a unit vector common to the tangent plane and the normal plane considered. In other words, to every direction in the tangent plane, characterized by a unit vector $\mathbf{i}$, there corresponds a normal plane containing it, and the curvature of the intersection of that plane with the surface is $s(\mathbf{i}, \mathbf{i})$.

Thus to every direction in the tangent plane there corresponds a definite number $s(\mathbf{i}, \mathbf{i})$, the curvature in that direction. As an exercise the reader may try to express the curvature corresponding to a direction in the tangent plane in terms of the angle that direction makes with the x axis.

Our aim is to generalize the above considerations so they would apply to the most general case, as far as the number of dimensions is concerned, both of the space and the configuration in it. Our program is to achieve this generalization in successive steps. First we studied a curve ($n = 1$) in a plane ($N = 2$), then a surface ($n = 2$) in ordinary space ($N = 3$). Now we shall consider a skew curve in that space, $n = 1$, $N = 3$. Under assumptions similar to those made above we can represent such a curve by equations $y = f(x)$, $z = g(x)$, where f and g are power series beginning respectively with quadratic terms

20.8 $$\tfrac{1}{2}a_2x^2, \qquad \tfrac{1}{2}b_2x^2.$$

If we change the y and z axes which lie in the normal plane of the curve to other axes in the same plane, the form of the development will not be changed, but, of course, the coefficients a_2, b_2 will assume new

values.   If, however, these coefficients are considered components of
a vector, the vector represented by them will be the same in all coordinate systems.   Designating this vector by **v**, it is clear that the curvature of the curve is characterized by the expression

20.9 $\frac{1}{2}\mathbf{v}x^2$.

This expression plays the part of expressions 20.1 and 20.2, which
have occurred in the two preceding situations.

21. Generalizations

In the preceding section we discussed configurations in the ordinary
space, where we could rely on our intuition.   That is, everybody can
conceive a plane curve, a surface, or a twisted curve, and we have at
our disposal physical objects (drawings, graphs, models) on which
measurements of the quantities of our theories may be successfully
identified.   In the following investigation it will not be possible to
rely on intuition, and the identifications, when they occur, will be of
a much less immediate nature.   It will therefore be necessary to rely
on analogies with the configurations studied in the preceding section
and on mathematical reasoning supported by formulas.

Consider what seems to be the next simplest case, a surface in four-
dimensional space.   It may be considered a generalization both of a
surface and of a curve in ordinary space.   In general, it is given by two
equations on the four coordinates.   In other words, it is defined in
four-space as the totality of points whose coordinates satisfy the two
equations $F(x, y, z, t) = 0$, $G(x, y, z, t) = 0$, where F, G are two functions subjected to certain restrictions that will be imposed presently.
A plane in four dimensions is defined as a surface which may be
expressed by two linear equations.   Although this definition is given
in terms of coordinates, it is invariant, because it can be proved that
if the equations are linear in one system of coordinates they remain
linear after a transformation.   Moreover, the equivalence of this
definition of the plane with that given in section 7 is easily recognized.
In the general case choose a point on the surface as the origin of
coordinates, solve the two equations for two of the coordinates, and
define, as the tangent plane at that point, the plane whose equations
result from omitting all but linear terms in the expansions.   Next
choose that plane as one of the coordinate planes so that the lowest
terms in the expansions are then the quadratic ones.   If the coordinates for which the equations appear as solved are denoted by x_3, x_4,
and the other two by x_1, x_2, the groups of quadratic terms in the two

expansions may be written

21.1 $\frac{1}{2}(a_{11}x_1^2 + 2a_{12}x_1x_2 + a_{22}x_2^2),$ $\frac{1}{2}(b_{11}x_1^2 + 2b_{12}x_1x_2 + b_{22}x_2^2).$

For every vector in the tangent plane of components x_1, x_2 this yields two numbers which may be considered the components of a vector in the normal x_3-x_4 plane, or this vector may be considered as given by a *vector* form

21.2 $\mathbf{v}_{11}x_1^2 + 2\mathbf{v}_{12}x_1x_2 + \mathbf{v}_{22}x_2^2,$

in which the coefficients $\mathbf{v}_{ij}$ are vectors of the normal plane whose components are a_{ij} and b_{ij} (along the x_3 and x_4 axes respectively). This expression assigns to every vector of the tangent plane a vector of the normal plane. As in an analogous case (compare 20.3), a more general expression

21.3 $\mathbf{s(x, y)} = \mathbf{v}_{11}x_1y_1 + \mathbf{v}_{12}x_1y_2 + \mathbf{v}_{21}x_2y_1 + \mathbf{v}_{22}x_2y_2,$

where

$$\mathbf{v}_{21} = \mathbf{v}_{12},$$

may be substituted for it, but although this is linear in each of the vectors $\mathbf{x}$ and $\mathbf{y}$ it is not a tensor, because the values of this expression are not numbers but vectors in the normal plane.

Here also the expression 20.5 may be formed, where it is understood that in the expansion of the determinant inner products now have to be used where previously ordinary products were employed. This change is made necessary by the fact that the values of the elements are vectors. In all other respects the same reasoning as before can be applied to the expression and the conclusion can be drawn that the relation 20.7 remains true where K is still a number, independent of the coordinate systems in the tangent and normal planes. However, after such coordinate systems have been chosen K can be calculated in terms of the coefficients of the vector form 21.3 by means of the formula

21.4 $K = \begin{vmatrix} \mathbf{v}_{11} & \mathbf{v}_{12} \\ \mathbf{v}_{21} & \mathbf{v}_{22} \end{vmatrix}.$

The important fact is that, although the expression 21.3 is a vector expression, and therefore does not furnish a tensor, the invariant 21.4 is a number. We term it, as before, the total curvature of the surface at the point considered.

In terms of the coefficients of the numerical forms 21.1 the total curvature K may be expressed as follows: expanding the determinant 21.4 we obtain $K = \mathbf{v}_{11} \cdot \mathbf{v}_{22} - \mathbf{v}_{21} \cdot \mathbf{v}_{12}$, where the term $\mathbf{v}_{11} \cdot \mathbf{v}_{22}$ is the inner product of the vectors v_{11} and v_{22} whose components are respectively a_{11}, b_{11} and a_{22}, b_{22} while the inner product $v_{11} \cdot v_{22}$ is then $a_{11}a_{22} + b_{11}b_{22}$; in the same way, the term $v_{21} \cdot v_{12}$ in the expression for K is $a_{12}a_{21} + b_{12}b_{21}$. Thus rearranging terms and using determinant notation, the following expression for K in terms of the a's and b's results:

$$21.41 \qquad K = \begin{vmatrix} a_{11} & a_{12} \\ a_{21} & a_{22} \end{vmatrix} + \begin{vmatrix} b_{11} & b_{12} \\ b_{21} & b_{22} \end{vmatrix}.$$

The next generalization is an easy one. Consider once again a surface ($n = 2$), but instead of a four-dimensional space let the space be of an arbitrary number of dimensions N and denote $N - n = N - 2$ by r so that we have, as before, a tangent plane, but instead of a normal plane, there is now a normal r-dimensional space, or an r-flat, as we shall say. Labeling the corresponding coordinates x_3, x_4, etc., or x_{2+k}, where k goes now from 1 to r instead of only taking the values 1 and 2, we obtain a vector form which may be written as in 21.2, except that now the v's are vectors of the normal flat and have r components each. These components may be distinguished by upper indices in parentheses. Denoting by I_k the r coordinate vectors in the normal flat, and by $a_{ij}^{(k)}$ the components corresponding to I_k of v_{ij}, these vectors can be written

$$21.5 \qquad v_{ij} = \sum_{k=1}^{r} I_k \cdot a\,_{ij}^{(k)},$$

while $s(x, y)$ becomes

$$21.6 \qquad \sum_{k=1}^{r} (a_{11}^{(k)}x_1y_1 + a_{12}^{(k)}x_1y_2 + a_{21}^{(k)}x_2y_1 + a_{22}^{(k)}x_2y_2)I_k.$$

Otherwise there is no change. The expression 21.4 can be formed as before, and it will be independent of the choice of the coordinates x_{2+k} because the inner products used in the expansion of the determinant are. Substituting, for $s(x, u)$ etc., the expressions 21.6, and using inner products in the evaluation of the determinant, we obtain

$$21.43 \qquad \begin{vmatrix} s(x, u) & s(x, v) \\ s(y, u) & s(y, v) \end{vmatrix} = \sum_{k=1}^{r} \begin{vmatrix} a_{ip}^{(k)}x_iu_p & a_{iq}^{(k)}x_iv_q \\ a_{jp}^{(k)}y_ju_p & a_{jq}^{(k)}y_jv_q \end{vmatrix},$$

where repeated subscripts imply summation from one to two corresponding to the tangent plane, and the summation with respect to k, corresponding to the r coordinates of the normal flat, is indicated in the usual fashion.   Each of the determinants corresponding to the different values of k is exactly of the same nature as 20.5, and so the reasoning which led from it to 20.7 applies to each of the determinants without change, and it is easy to see that formula 20.7 continues to hold.   We use this formula to define K, which we shall continue to call total curvature.

Now we come to the last generalization.   Consider, in a space of an arbitrary number of dimensions N, a *curved space* of n dimensions which by definition is the totality of points whose coordinates satisfy $N - n = r$ equations

21.7 $F_k(x_1, x_2, \cdots x_N) = 0 \quad (k = 1, 2, \cdots r).$

Assume that for every point in the curved space these equations can be solved for r of the coordinates and that these solutions can be expanded into power series in the remaining n coordinates, which converge in the neighborhood of the point selected.   By a transformation of coordinates it may be arranged so that these expansions begin with second-degree terms so that

21.71 $x_{n+k} = \frac{1}{2} a_{ij}^{(k)} x_i x_j +$ terms of higher degree,

where the summation indicated by repeated indices now goes from 1 to n.   The subspace defined by the first n coordinate axes will be called the tangent flat space at the point considered; and the subspace corresponding to the remaining r coordinate axes, the normal flat space at that point.

As before, use the coefficients $a_{ij}^{(k)}$ to form the expressions

21.8 $a_{ij}^{(k)} x_i y_j,$

where x_i, y_j are the components of two vectors of the tangent flat; and combine these expressions into a vector expression

21.9 $$\mathbf{s}(\mathbf{x}, \mathbf{y}) = \sum_{k=1}^{r} a_{ij}^{(k)} x_i y_j \cdot \mathbf{I}_k.$$

It is natural to try to generalize the idea of total curvature.   The expression 20.5 can be formed, but, and *this is important*, the transformation 20.7 does not apply, since it was based essentially on the fact that $n = 2$.

22. The Riemann tensor

The way out of this difficulty is very simple.   Although a relation analogous to 20.7 does not hold we still may consider the expression which takes the place of its left-hand side, namely 21.43. This expression defines a numerical valued function of the four vectors **x, y, u, v,** and it is easy to show that this function is linear in each of the vector arguments (we omit this proof because the result will follow later from formula 22.8). It is therefore a tensor of rank *four*, which will be called the Riemann tensor and denoted by $R(\mathbf{x}, \mathbf{y}; \mathbf{u}, \mathbf{v})$, so that

22.1 $$R(\mathbf{x}, \mathbf{y}; \mathbf{u}, \mathbf{v}) = \begin{vmatrix} s(\mathbf{x}, \mathbf{u}) & s(\mathbf{x}, \mathbf{v}) \\ s(\mathbf{y}, \mathbf{u}) & s(\mathbf{y}, \mathbf{v}) \end{vmatrix}.$$

We have, therefore, at every point of the curved space a tensor of rank four instead of a number. Since it is connected with the second-degree terms of the expansions 21.71, it characterizes, at least in part, the deviation of the expressions of the x_{n+k} from linearity, or of our space from flatness. Since the Riemann tensor tells us, then, something about the curvature of the curved space, it is often called the *curvature tensor.*

This situation is similar to that of section 20. There the curvature of a curve was a number while that of a surface was characterized by a tensor. From this tensor a number K was derived which, at least partially, expressed the curvature of a surface by a number. Now in higher-dimensional curved spaces we again have a tensor but this time it expresses, as we shall prove, internal properties. In the preceding situation we succeeded in interpreting the tensor $s(\mathbf{x}, \mathbf{y})$ given by formula 20.3 in terms of curvatures of certain curves on the surface, and we found that the value $s(\mathbf{i}, \mathbf{i})$ gives the curvature of the normal section determined by the unit vector **i** and the normal to the surface. Is it possible to interpret the Riemann tensor in an analogous way as giving the total curvatures of some surfaces on our curved space? This is a natural question to ask, and the answer is affirmative. We shall prove, in fact, that certain values of the Riemann tensor give us total curvatures of surfaces situated on the curved space. Let **i, j** be two arbitrary mutually perpendicular unit vectors of the tangent flat, and choose a set of coordinate vectors so that **i, j** are the first two of them. Pass through **i, j** and the normal flat, i.e., through the r vectors $\mathbf{I}_k$, a flat space of $2 + r$ dimensions. Its points will be those points of the N-space whose coordinates $x_3, x_4, \cdots x_n$ vanish. The intersection of this flat space with the given curved space will be a surface, i.e., a two-dimensional curved space, because the coordinates of its points must satisfy the r equations of the curved space (21.7) and $n - 2$ equations

22.2 $$x_3 = 0, \quad x_4 = 0, \cdots, \quad x_n = 0,$$

or, altogether $N - n + (n - 2) = N - 2$ equations. This surface may be considered a surface of the $r + 2$ dimensional flat space 22.2. Its equations in that space will be obtained by setting $x_3 = x_4 = \cdots$ $x_n = 0$ in equations 21.71 of the curved space (just as the equation of the normal section of a surface in the x-z plane was obtained—compare the discussion preceding formula 20.11—by setting $y = 0$ in the equation of the surface). These equations will then become

22.3 $x_{n+k} = \frac{1}{2}(a^{(k)}x_1{}^2 + 2a_{12}^{(k)}x_1x_2 + a_{22}^{(k)}x_2{}^2) +$ terms of higher

$$\text{degree,}$$

and the total curvature of this surface is

$$\begin{vmatrix} \mathbf{v}_{11} & \mathbf{v}_{12} \\ \mathbf{v}_{21} & \mathbf{v}_{22} \end{vmatrix}$$

with

$$\mathbf{v}_{ij} = a_{ij}^{(k)} \cdot \mathbf{I}_k.$$

However, $\mathbf{v}_{11} = \mathbf{s}(\mathbf{i}, \mathbf{i}), \mathbf{v}_{12} = \mathbf{s}(\mathbf{i}, \mathbf{j}), \mathbf{v}_{21} = \mathbf{s}(\mathbf{j}, \mathbf{i}), \mathbf{v}_{22} = \mathbf{s}(\mathbf{j}, \mathbf{j})$, so that

$$K = \begin{vmatrix} \mathbf{s}(\mathbf{i}, \mathbf{i}) & \mathbf{s}(\mathbf{i}, \mathbf{j}) \\ \mathbf{s}(\mathbf{j}, \mathbf{i}) & \mathbf{s}(\mathbf{j}, \mathbf{j}) \end{vmatrix},$$

which is $R(\mathbf{i}, \mathbf{j}; \mathbf{i}, \mathbf{j})$, and the statement is proved.

The situation is analogous to that in section 20. There a unit vector $\mathbf{i}$ in the tangent plane to a surface determines a line that together with the normal determines a normal plane, and the intersection of this normal plane with the surface is a curve whose curvature is $s(\mathbf{i}, \mathbf{i})$. Here two mutually perpendicular unit vectors $\mathbf{i}, \mathbf{j}$ in the tangent flat to a curved space determine a plane that together with the normal 2-flat determines a normal $(r + 2)$-flat, and the intersection of this $(r + 2)$-flat with the curved space is a surface whose (total) curvature is $R(\mathbf{i}, \mathbf{j}; \mathbf{i}, \mathbf{j})$. We see then that the Riemann tensor plays in a curved space a role analogous to that played by the tensor $s(\mathbf{x}, \mathbf{y})$ in an ordinary surface. Our expectations then are fulfilled. However, for the purposes of identification with the complete tensor T_{ij} we need a tensor of the *second* rank. This we shall later construct from the tensor $R(\mathbf{x}, \mathbf{y}; \mathbf{u}, \mathbf{v})$ by applying to it the operation of contraction.

In the meantime let us study the Riemann tensor, as we have defined it. The Riemann tensor is not a general tensor of rank four. It satisfies the relations

22.41 $R(\mathbf{x}, \mathbf{y}; \mathbf{u}, \mathbf{v}) = -R(\mathbf{y}, \mathbf{x}; \mathbf{u}, \mathbf{v}) = -R(\mathbf{x}, \mathbf{y}; \mathbf{v}, \mathbf{u})$,

22.42 $R(\mathbf{x}, \mathbf{y}; \mathbf{u}, \mathbf{v}) = R(\mathbf{u}, \mathbf{v}; \mathbf{x}, \mathbf{y})$,

22.43 $R(\mathbf{x}, \mathbf{y}; \mathbf{u}, \mathbf{v}) + R(\mathbf{x}, \mathbf{u}; \mathbf{v}, \mathbf{y}) + R(\mathbf{x}, \mathbf{v}; \mathbf{y}, \mathbf{u}) = 0$, as it is easy to verify by using the definition 22.1. The first of these relations says that R is antisymmetric in each of the pairs of the vector arguments; and the second, that it is symmetric in the two pairs.

If we introduce a coordinate system in the tangent flat, by picking four coordinate vectors i, j, k, 1 or e_1, e_2, e_3, e_4, and represent the vector arguments (as in section 10) in the form $x = e_i x_i$, etc., the substitution of these expressions into $R(x, y; u, v)$, with the use of linearity as defined in 10.6, enables us to write it as

22.5 $$R_{ij;pq} x_i y_j u_p v_q$$

where

22.6 $$R_{ij;pq} = R(e_i, e_j; e_p e_q).$$

The quantities 22.6 are the components of the Riemann tensor in the coordinate system chosen. The relations 22.4 can be written in components as

22.71 $$R_{ij;pq} = -R_{ji;pq} = -R_{ij;qp},$$

22.72 $$R_{ij;pq} = R_{pq;ij},$$

22.73 $$R_{ij;pq} + R_{ip;qj} + R_{iq;jp} = 0.$$

Exercise 1. How many independent components does a Riemann tensor have for $n = 2$, $n = 3$, $n = 4$; for a general n?

Exercise 2. Prove that, if $R(x, y; x, y)$ is given for all x and y, one can find all the values $R(x, y; u, v)$.

The vectors of the flat spaces tangent to the curved space may be characterized in terms of the space itself, for example by giving direction and length. They are accessible, as we may say, to beings who live in the space and for whom points outside the space do not exist. Normal vectors, such as the function $s(x, y)$ etc., are, on the contrary, not accessible to the inhabitants of the space. We shall be concerned primarily with the consideration of these internal properties, which are accessible to the inhabitants. Later in the course of our investigation we shall have to use the expression for the Riemann tensor in terms of the coefficients $a_{ij}^{(k)}$, and we shall conclude this section by deducing it.

Substituting the expression 21.9 for s into 22.1 and using 22.5 for the left-hand side, it follows that

22.8 $$R_{ij;pq} x_i y_j u_p v_q = \begin{vmatrix} \Sigma a_{ip}^{(k)} x_i u_p I_k & \Sigma a_{iq}^{(k)} x_i v_q I_k \\ \Sigma a_{jp}^{(k)} y_j u_p I_k & \Sigma a_{jq}^{(k)} y_j v_q I_k \end{vmatrix}.$$

This determinant may be written as the sum of r^2 determinants, of which, however, only r are different from zero, namely, those in which the same $\mathbf{I}$ appears in the two columns.   In the expansions of the others all terms vanish since they involve products of different and therefore mutually perpendicular $\mathbf{I}$'s.   The remainder is (compare 21.43)

$$\sum_{k=1}^{r} \begin{vmatrix} a_{ip}^{(k)} x_i u_p \mathbf{I}_k & a_{iq}^{(k)} x_i v_q \mathbf{I}_k \\ a_{jp}^{(k)} y_j u_p \mathbf{I}_k & a_{jq}^{(k)} y_j v_q \mathbf{I}_k \end{vmatrix} = \sum_{k=1}^{r} \begin{vmatrix} a_{ip}^{(k)} x_i u_p & a_{iq}^{(k)} x_i v_q \\ a_{jp}^{(k)} y y_j u_p & a_{jq}^{(k)} y_j v_q \end{vmatrix}$$

because the $\mathbf{I}$'s are unit vectors and $\mathbf{I}_k \cdot \mathbf{I}_k = 1$ (no summation is implied here by repeated index), or

$$\sum_{k=1}^{r} \begin{vmatrix} a_{ip}^{(k)} & a_{iq}^{(k)} \\ a_{jp}^{(k)} & a_{jp}^{(k)} \end{vmatrix} x_i y_j u_p v_q.$$

Comparing this to the left-hand side of 22.8 we have the required expression

22.9
$$R_{ij;pq} = \sum_{k=1}^{r} \begin{vmatrix} a_{ip}^{(k)} & a_{iq}^{(k)} \\ a_{jp}^{(k)} & a_{jq}^{(k)} \end{vmatrix}.$$

REMARK.   This formula is general.   It applies, of course, to the special case of ordinary surface in ordinary space.   In this case $r = 1$ (so that we can leave off the superscripts k), and the subscripts take only the values 1 and 2.   When $i = 1$, $j = 2$, $p = 1$, $q = 2$ we have

$$R_{12,12} = \begin{vmatrix} a_{11} & a_{12} \\ a_{21} & a_{22} \end{vmatrix}.$$

That is, the component $R_{12,12}$ of the Riemann tensor is in this special case the total curvature of the surface and formula 20.4 appears as a special case of 22.9.

23. Points and vectors in general coordinates

In the last section we determined how to associate a tensor of rank four with every point of a curved space.   For our physical interpretation we need a tensor of rank two.   However, we know how to obtain a tensor of rank two from a tensor of rank four by applying the operation of contraction.   The result we shall call the "contracted Riemann tensor," and we shall identify it with the complete tensor T.   The first question we have to answer in this connection is whether this contracted Riemann tensor satisfies equation 12.4, viz., $\partial_j T_{ij} = 0$. However, although we have introduced tensors in a curved space, or, more precisely, tensors in the tangent flats to a curved space, our method does not permit us to differentiate these tensors because we use a different coordinate system for different points of the curved space. Thus we cannot express the changes of quantities from point to point in terms of their dependence on the coordinates. If we want to make statements about such changes, i.e., if we want to speak of derivatives or write down differential equations, it seems that we must introduce a coordinate system which would apply to the whole or at least a portion of the curved space.

One way of introducing such a system of coordinates on a curved surface (the generalization to curved space will be treated later) is to consider the projection of that curved surface on a plane. If the surface is not too pathological and if we consider a small enough piece of the surface, no two points of that piece will have the same projection, so that the point can be given by its projection, or by the coordinates of its projection. If a surface is given by the equation $z = f(x_1, x_2)$, for example, as in section 20, we can specify a point P on the surface by giving the numbers x_1, x_2. We can say that we use the x_1-x_2 plane as a map of the surface. But, of course, this mapping by projection is only one concrete procedure for introducing coordinates on the surface, i.e., one way of introducing a method of specifying the position of a point on a surface by giving two numbers. Often we do not have to say how we map the surface on the plane, and in fact that mapping is not essential. All we are interested in is the method of specifying the position of a point by two numbers. Everyone knows the example of geographical coordinates, where a position of a point on the surface of a sphere is given by latitude and longitude. Of course, if we have such a pair of numbers we may interpret them as ordinary coordinates on a plane, and then we again have a mapping of a surface onto a plane.

Summarizing and generalizing we will specify the position of a point P in a curved space by n numbers, and we will not be interested in how these numbers were obtained. The only important thing is that to every point (of a certain portion of the space) there corresponds an n-upple of numbers $x^i(i = 1 \cdots n)$ and that to every n-upple (within a certain range) there corresponds a point.

REMARK 1. From now on, for reasons which will appear later, we shall use superscripts instead of subscripts in denoting coordinates.

REMARK 2. In the case of cartesian coordinates we use a system of mutually perpendicular lines, the coordinate axes, in terms of which we assign numbers to points. In the general case there are no coordinate axes, and when we speak of a system of coordinates all we have in mind is that there is a method of somehow assigning n-upples of numbers to points.

Since a point is determined by its coordinates it can be thought of as a function of these coordinates and we shall use the notation $P(x^1, x^2, \cdots x^n)$ for the point of coordinates $x^i(i = 1 \cdots n)$.

Next we shall discuss the question of representation of *vectors*. We could, of course, introduce a system of representation of vectors entirely independent of the system of representation of points, that is we could introduce at every point of a curved surface two mutually perpendicular unit vectors on the tangent plane at that point, and express any other vector on that tangent plane as a linear combination of these two. But to use a notation for vectors independent of that for points would clearly be inconvenient now since points and vectors are closely related in the process of differentiation. To introduce coordinate vectors which are related to the coordinates of points observe that through every point on a surface there pass two curves: one, on which x^2 is constant; and one on which x^1 is constant. Introduce as parameters x^1 along the first and x^2 along the second. If the coordinates of the point are a and b so that the point itself is represented by $P(a, b)$, the two curves will be represented by $P(x^1, b)$ and by $P(a, x^2)$. The tangent vectors to these two curves at the point $P(a, b)$ lie in the tangent plane to the surface, and it is these two vectors that will be used as coordinate vectors for that plane. These vectors are obtained by differentiation with respect to the respective parameters and will be denoted by c_1 and c_2, so that

$$\mathbf{c}_1 = \partial_1 P, \quad \mathbf{c}_2 = \partial_2 P.$$

Any vector in the tangent plane (we usually think of these vectors as having initial points at the point of tangency) will be a linear combination of these two, so that, if u^1 and u^2 denote the coefficients of the linear combination representing a vector $\mathbf{u}$,

$$\mathbf{u} = u^1\mathbf{c}_1 + u^2\mathbf{c}_2 = u^i\mathbf{c}_i.$$

There is nothing in the foregoing except ease of visualization that restricts the above argument to a two-dimensional surface in ordinary space. Then we may consider, as we did in sections 21 and 22, an n-dimensional curved space. Its points will be given as stated before, by n numbers $x^i(i = 1 \cdots n)$, so that they will be functions $P(x^1 \cdots x^n)$ of n variables. The partial derivatives

23.1 $$\mathbf{c}_i = \partial_i P$$

will determine n vectors in the tangent flat at each point; and these c's will serve as coordinate vectors in terms of which any vector $\mathbf{u}$ of that flat, or of the curved space, will be represented by

23.2 $\mathbf{u} = \mathbf{c}_i u^i.$

REMARK. The reader will have observed that now indices sometimes appear as superscripts or in the upper position, and sometimes
as subscripts or in the lower position. This distinction is essential, as
will appear later. In fact, sometimes the same letter with the same
index will have a different meaning depending on the position of the
index.

If the coordinate system in the curved space could be chosen in such
a way that the coordinate vectors $\mathbf{c}_i = \partial_i P$ formed an orthonormal set,
it would not be necessary to change anything in the discussion of
tensors as given in section 10. Unfortunately this is, in general,
impossible, and so it will be necessary to use coordinate vectors that
are not perpendicular unit vectors. The situation explains the remark
of section 8 (after formula 8.12) that the use of an òrthonormal set
is not always convenient.

It will therefore become necessary to revise the representation of
tensors introduced in Chapter 2.

Exercise. Show that if coordinates r, θ, ϕ are introduced by the formulas

$$x = r \sin \theta \cos \phi, \quad y = r \sin \theta \sin \phi, \quad z = r \cos \theta$$

the vectors $\mathbf{c}_1$, $\mathbf{c}_2$, $\mathbf{c}_3$ are orthogonal in pairs and that their squares are respectively
1, r^2, and $r^2 \sin^2 \theta$.

24. Tensors in general coordinates

As the definition of tensor given in section 10 was independent of
coordinates it can be applied at this point. The tensor components,
of course, depend on the coordinate system, but their definition did
not depend on the use of an *orthonormal* set of coordinate vectors.
As previously, we can write, for example, a tensor of rank two, in a
general set of coordinate vectors, as

24.1 $\phi(\mathbf{x}, \mathbf{y}) = \phi(x^i \mathbf{c}_i, y^j \mathbf{c}_j) = \phi_{ij} x^i y^j,$

where

24.11 $\phi_{ij} = \phi(\mathbf{c}_i, \mathbf{c}_j).$

The reader should note, however, the position of the indices: the vector
components have superscripts, and the tensor components have
subscripts.

The fact that the coordinate vectors $\mathbf{c}_i$ no longer satisfy the condition 8.3 of orthonormality affects the representation of the inner

product which (compare exercise 3 of section 10) is a tensor of rank two.   According to formula 24.11 its components are given by

24.2 $$g_{ij} = \mathbf{c}_i \cdot \mathbf{c}_j$$

(as compared to δ_{ij} for an orthonormal system), and the inner product of the vectors $\mathbf{x}$ and $\mathbf{y}$ is

24.21 $$\mathbf{x} \cdot \mathbf{y} = g_{ij}x^iy^j.$$

A further difference will appear in the relation between a vector and a tensor of rank one.   In section 10 a correspondence was established by the formula $\phi(\mathbf{x}) = \mathbf{v} \cdot \mathbf{x}$, and it was shown that the vector $\mathbf{v}$ and the tensor ϕ have the same components.   This last statement is no longer true if the $\mathbf{c}$'s are not orthonormal.   In fact, the components of $\phi(x)$ are

24.22 $$\phi_i = \phi(\mathbf{c}_i) = \mathbf{v} \cdot \mathbf{c}_i,$$

or, if we set $\mathbf{v} = \mathbf{c}_j v^j$, $\phi_i = \mathbf{c}_i\mathbf{c}_j v^j$.   Finally, using the notation 24.2, they may be expressed as

24.3 $$\phi_i = g_{ij}v^j.$$

This is the relation between the components of a vector and the components of the corresponding tensor of rank one.   When the $\mathbf{c}$'s are orthonormal the g's are the δ's, and we obtain our earlier result that then the components of ϕ and $\mathbf{v}$ are the same.

Formula 24.3 permits the calculation of the ϕ_i when the v^j are given. If the ϕ_i are given and it is desired to calculate the v^j, it is necessary to consider 24.3 as a system of equations with v^j as the unknowns, g_{ij} as the coefficients, and ϕ_i as the constant terms.   By the theory of determinants the expressions for the v^j are fractions whose denominator is the determinant of the g's and whose numerators are obtained from this determinant by replacing the elements of certain columns by the constant terms, or they are linear combinations of the constant terms multiplied by certain cofactors of the determinant.   Denoting the determinant by g and these cofactors by G_{ij}, one has

$$v^j = \frac{G_{ji}}{g} \phi_i.$$

The standard notation is $g^{ij} = G_{ij}/g$, and so we can now write

$$v^j = g^{ji}\phi_i.$$

Exercise 1.   Prove that $g_{ij} = g_{ji}$ and $g^{ij} = g^{ji}$.
Exercise 2.   Prove that $g_{ij}g^{jk} = \delta_{ik}$.

Furthermore, it is customary to denote the components of a vector and those of the corresponding tensor of rank one by the same letter, using upper indices or superscripts for the vector components and lower indices or subscripts for the tensor components. Then the above relations take on the final form

24.4 $$v_i = g_{ij}v^j, \qquad v^j = g^{ji}v_i.$$

Very often instead of distinguishing between "a vector and the corresponding tensor of rank one" it is more convenient to think of them as two different representations of the same thing, and then they are referred to as *contra*variant and *co*variant vectors respectively or as contravariant and covariant components of the same vector.

REMARK. The correspondence between vectors and tensors of order one is established by means of the inner product, and so in a discussion that does not assume postulate IV (affine geometry) the preceding is not applicable. As a matter of fact, identification between vectors and tensors of rank one is equivalent to the introduction of inner multiplication (see section 10).

It may seem strange that we should use two different representations, the contravariant and the covariant, for the same thing, but, as we shall see now, it sometimes simplifies things.

It was shown before that, if two vectors u and v are given by their (as we say now) contravariant components, their inner product can be written as $g_{ij}u^iv^j$. But using 24.4 this may also be written as

24.23 $$u^iv_i \quad \text{or} \quad u_jv^j.$$

In words, the *inner product is equal to the sum of products of corresponding components of two vectors*. This rule is almost as simple as it was for an orthonormal system, but of course now *one vector must be given by its contravariant and the other by its covariant components*. This is an example of the advantage to be gained by a judicious choice of the type of components of vectors. Now we want to achieve a similar advantage for tensors.

In formula 24.1, $\phi(\mathbf{x}, \mathbf{y}) = \phi_{ij}x^iy^j$, the vector arguments were given by their contravariant components. However, $\phi(\mathbf{x}, \mathbf{y})$ can also be calculated when $\mathbf{x}$ and $\mathbf{y}$ are given by their covariant components x_i, y_i: we can, by the second of formulas 24.4, find the contravariant components and substitute them into 24.1 to obtain

$$\phi(\mathbf{x}, \mathbf{y}) = \phi_{ij}g^{ik}x_kg^{js}y_s = \phi^{ks}x_ky_s,$$

where

24.41 $$\phi^{ks} = g^{ik}g^{js}\phi_{ij}.$$

In the calculation of the value of a tensor in terms of the covariant components of the vector arguments the quantities ϕ^{ks} play the same role as the quantities ϕ_{ks} did when contravariant components of the vector arguments were given. The ϕ^{ks} are called the contravariant components of the tensor ϕ, and the original components ϕ_{ij} are called the covariant components. Similarly,

$$24.42 \qquad\qquad \phi^{ksm} = g^{ik}g^{js}g^{pm}\phi_{ijp}$$

will be termed the contravariant components of a tensor whose covariant components are ϕ_{ijp}. (It is probably superfluous to add that it is the position of the indices, not the letters used to denote them, that makes the difference.)

It may happen that some of the vector arguments of a tensor are given by their contravariant and some by their covariant components. If, for example, the first argument in $\phi(\mathbf{x}, \mathbf{y})$ is given by the components x_i and the second by y^j, we obtain

$$\phi(x, y) = \phi^i{}_j x_i y^j,$$

where

$$24.43 \qquad\qquad \phi^i{}_j = g^{ki}\phi_{kj}.$$

These components are called *mixed*, and it is easily understood what is meant by $\phi_i{}^j$.

Remark. We know that, when we use an orthonormal system, the components of a symmetric tensor are symmetric in the indices. This is true also in the general case for contravariant as well as covariant components, but *not for mixed components.*

Looking at formulas 24.4, 24.41, 24.42, and 24.43 from a purely formal point of view we may describe them by saying that they show how to raise or to lower an index. In 24.43 the first index of ϕ on the right-hand side of the equation is below, and on the left side it is above. In order to raise the index, ϕ_{kj} is multiplied by g with two upper indices one of which is the same as the index to be raised (and of course this implies that summation takes place). The reader will see that this procedure applies whenever an index is being raised, and that in lowering an index the same rule is followed, except that g with two lower indices is employed.

Although the operation of contraction was introduced in section 10 with the aid of an orthonormal system its definition was independent of that. It was based on the fact that a tensor $\omega(\mathbf{x}, \mathbf{y})$ could be presented as the sum of products of the type $(\mathbf{u}\mathbf{x})(\mathbf{v}\mathbf{y})$, and it consisted in replacing every such product by the inner product $\mathbf{u} \cdot \mathbf{v}$. Now if

$\omega(\mathbf{x}, \mathbf{y})$ is considered as given by its components ω_{ij} then $(\mathbf{ux})(\mathbf{vy})$ will be given by $u_i v_j$ and the inner product will have to be written as $g^{ij} u_i v_j$, so that:

24.5   the contraction of ω_{ij} is $g^{ij}\omega_{ij}$.

Of course, if the tensor is given in contravariant form ω^{ij}, the contraction is $g_{ij}\omega^{ij}$. However, the situation is simplest when the tensor is given in mixed form, for the contraction of $\omega^i{}_j$ is simply $\omega^i{}_i$. This is another example of the advantages to be gained by proper positioning of the indices. For a tensor of higher rank the two indices with respect to which contraction is performed must be in opposite positions. If they are not, one of them must be lowered or raised.

Exercise 3. Show that in all the formulas of this and the preceding section summation may be interpreted as contraction.

For an orthonormal set of coordinate vectors $g_{ij} = \delta_{ij}$, and formulas 24.4 state that the covariant components are equal to the contravariant components (this is only another way of saying that in the orthonormal case a vector and the corresponding tensor of rank one have the same components). But this applies only if the coordinate set is orthonormal in the *original* sense, that is, when the vectors in addition to being mutually perpendicular have square equal to *plus* 1. When some unit vectors are of square -1 it is no longer true that $g_{ij} = \delta_{ij}$. If, for example, $(\mathbf{c}_4)^2 = -1$, then $g_{44} = \mathbf{c}_4 \cdot \mathbf{c}_4 = -1$ whereas $\delta_{44} = 1$. However, the formulas for the inner product remain true no matter what the character of the space is, whether there are or there are no vectors of negative square, and whether postulate V or postulate V′ holds. When we cease using orthonormal sets, as we are forced to do for curved spaces, we gain the advantage of a simple notation which does not introduce complex numbers—at least in formulas or vectors. Later it will be shown that this is true also for differential equations.

Exercise 4. Show that in the case of coordinate vectors which satisfy the relations $\mathbf{c}_i \mathbf{c}_j = 0$ when $i \neq j$, $(\mathbf{c}_1)^2 = (\mathbf{c}_2)^2 = (\mathbf{c}_3)^2 = 1$, $(\mathbf{c}_4)^2 = -1$, raising the indices 1, 2, 3 does not change the components, but that raising (or lowering) the index 4 changes the sign of the component.

In view of the importance of the tensor g_{ij} we shall indicate here another formula in which it appears. In flat space we had a formula 13.1 for the length of a curve. If we consider a curve in general coordinates we may represent it by $P(x^1, \cdots, x^n)$, where the x^i are functions of a parameter p.   A tangent vector will be given by

$$\frac{dP}{dp} = \partial_i P \frac{dx^i}{dp} = \mathbf{c}_i \frac{dx^i}{dp};$$

we see that dx^i/dp are the contravariant components of the tangent vector.   The expression under the radical in 13.1 is the square of that vector, that is, the inner product of that vector with itself.   According to 24.21, formula 13.1 becomes then

24.5 $$s = \int_{p_1}^{p} \sqrt{g_{ij} \frac{dx^i}{dp} \frac{dx^j}{dp}} \, dp.$$

This formula involves three inverse operations: integration, taking the square root, and division.   It is preferable, in general, not to use inverse operations; if we eliminate them here the formula may be written

24.51 $$ds^2 = g_{ij} \, dx^i \, dx^j.$$

This formula expresses the same situation as 24.5.   It is often used to indicate briefly what values are assigned to the g's; in other words, instead of giving, in a special case, separately the values of the various g's, one writes the formula 24.51 using these values.

Since 24.51 serves to calculate the lengths of curves one says that it determines the metric of the space.   The tensor g_{ij} is often called the metric tensor, or the fundamental tensor.

25. Differentiation in general coordinates

In section 10 differentiation of tensors was defined in flat space, in which points, vectors, and tensors were represented in cartesian coordinates.   In this section we will discuss the passage from a tensor to its differential in flat space, in a general system of coordinates.   In the next section the necessary modifications required by the transition to curved space will be introduced.

As in section 10 we begin by considering the differential of a tensor field f of rank zero.   Note first that f stands not so much for the functional dependence as for the value of the function.   Strictly speaking, in one coordinate system, f is represented by one function, let us say $F(x^1, \cdots x^n)$, and in another coordinate system the same quantity f will be represented by a different function $G(\bar{x}^1, \cdots \bar{x}^n)$ of the new variables.   Of course the x_i are functions of the $\bar{x}_i$, and vice versa, and it will always be assumed that in a formula where both the x^i and the $\bar{x}^i$ appear they have corresponding values so that

$$f = F(x^1, \cdots x^n) = G(\bar{x}^1, \cdots \bar{x}^n).$$

When two coordinate systems are used, it is, of course, assumed that the x's are differentiable functions of the $\bar{x}$'s. Thus the two sets of partial derivatives $\partial x^i/\partial \bar{x}^j$ and $\partial \bar{x}^i/\partial x^j$ exist. If the derivatives $\partial \omega/\partial x^i$ of any quantity ω are given with respect to one system, the derivatives of ω with respect to the other system will be obtained by the formula of differentiation of a function of functions. Thus

25.1
$$\frac{\partial \omega}{\partial \bar{x}^i} = \frac{\partial \omega}{\partial x^j} \frac{\partial x^j}{\partial \bar{x}^i}.$$

Note also the identity

25.11
$$\frac{\partial x^i}{\partial \bar{x}^j} \frac{\partial \bar{x}^j}{\partial x^k} = \delta_{ik},$$

which may be verified by noticing that the left member is the derivative of x^i with respect to x^k of the same system and is, because the x's are independent of each other, *one* when $k = i$, and *zero* when x^k and x^i are different coordinates.

Just as the same quantity f is represented by different functions in different coordinate systems, the same vector is represented by different components because corresponding to different coordinate systems there are different coordinate vectors. Corresponding to the x coordinates the set of coordinate vectors is $c_i = \partial P/\partial x^i$, while corresponding to the $\bar{x}$ coordinates the coordinate vectors are $\bar{c}_j = \partial P/\partial \bar{x}^j$. The relations between the c's and the $\bar{c}$'s are, according to 25.1,

25.12
$$\bar{c}_i = c_j \frac{\partial x^j}{\partial \bar{x}^i}, \qquad c_j = \bar{c}_i \frac{\partial \bar{x}^i}{\partial x^j}.$$

Thus, the same vector dP may be represented in the two following ways:

25.13
$$dP = c_i \, dx^i = \bar{c}_j \, d\bar{x}^j,$$

and the relation between the dx^i and $d\bar{x}^j$ is easily seen to be

25.14
$$dx^i = \frac{\partial x^i}{\partial \bar{x}^j} \, d\bar{x}^j, \qquad d\bar{x}^j = \frac{\partial \bar{x}^j}{\partial x^i} \, dx^i.$$

Using formulas 25.1, 25.14, and 25.11 it is easily seen that the expression $\partial f/\partial x^i \cdot dx^i$ is equal to the expression $\partial f/\partial \bar{x}^j \cdot d\bar{x}^j$. This expression is thus invariant under coordinate transformation, and it expresses the same tensor of rank one in all coordinate systems. It is called, as is well known, the differential. Once these things are clear it is no longer necessary to use different coordinate systems, and so we shall use the notation $\partial_i f$ for $\partial f/\partial x_i$. The differential of the tensor of rank zero, f, is then in general coordinates

$$df = \partial_i f \cdot dx^i.$$

The differentiation of a tensor of higher rank was achieved first by considering the vector arguments as *constant* (that is, the same in all points); second, by differentiating the resulting quantity to obtain a new vector argument; and, finally, by restoring variability to those vector arguments that were present before. It was found that the components of the new tensor were obtained by differentiating the components of the given tensor with respect to the coordinates.

In cartesian coordinates a constant vector has constant components, but that unfortunately is not so in general coordinates. In fact, the components v^i of a vector are the coefficients of the linear combination $v^i c_i$ which represents the vector, and, since the c's change from point to point, the *same vector* in different points will be represented by *different components*. In order to apply our procedure of differentiation of tensors it therefore becomes necessary to find out how to represent a constant vector field. If the vector **v** is constant its derivatives must be zero, so that

25.2 $\qquad 0 = \partial_j \mathbf{v} = \partial_j(v^i c_i) = (\partial_j v^i) \cdot c_i + v_i \cdot \partial_j c_i.$

The quantities $\partial_j c_i$ play an important part in what follows. For every j and i the derivative $\partial_j c_i$ is a vector, and as such it may be presented as a linear combination of the c's. Denote the coefficients of this linear combination by Γ^k_{ij}, so that

25.3 $\qquad \partial_j c_i = \Gamma^k_{ij} c_k.$

If these relations are inserted into the above equation which expresses the constancy of a vector field (and if the summation index i is replaced by k in the first term), one obtains

$$(\partial_j v^k + v^i \Gamma^k_{ij}) c_k = 0,$$

whence, since the c's are independent,

25.31 $\qquad \partial_j v^k + \Gamma^k_{ij} v^i = 0, \quad$ or $\quad \partial_j v^k = -\Gamma^k_{ij} v^i.$

The meaning of this relation is that the components of a *constant* vector field are, in general, *variable* and satisfy the above differential equation.

Given a tensor field $\phi(\mathbf{v})$, represented by $\phi_i v^i$, let us determine its

differential.   In the first step $\mathbf{v}$ is kept fixed so that the differential
will be

25.32 $\partial_j(\phi_k v^k) \cdot dx^j$.

Now

$$\partial_j(\phi_k v^k) = (\partial_j \phi_k)v^k + \phi_k \cdot \partial_j v^k,$$

and, since $\mathbf{v}$ is a constant vector field, we must use 25.31 to obtain

$$\partial_j(\phi_k v^k) = (\partial_j \phi_k)v^k - \phi_k \Gamma_{ij}^k v^i.$$

Replacing the summation index k by i in the first term, this becomes

$$(\partial_j \phi_i - \Gamma_{ij}^k \phi_k)v^i,$$

so that its substitution into 25.32 yields

$$(\partial_j \phi_i - \Gamma_{ij}^k \phi_k)v^i \, dx^j.$$

This is the tensor of rank two obtained from the tensor of rank one,
$\phi_i v^i$, by differentiation.   It appears, as it should, as a bilinear form
with two vector arguments—the old one v^i to which we now restore
its variability, and the new one dx^j which appears as a result of differentiation.   In cartesian coordinates the components of the differential
are the derivatives of the components of the given tensor, whereas
here the components of the differential are

25.33 $\partial_j \phi_i - \Gamma_{ij}^k \phi_k$.

They are *not* the derivatives of the components; the derivatives of the
components must be corrected to yield the components of the differential.   Since these components of the differential play an important
part they deserve a name and a notation.   They are called the *covariant derivatives* of the components ϕ_i, and they are denoted by $\phi_{i,j}$.
In words, a component of the differential of a given tensor is denoted
by placing a comma and a new index beyond the index of the component of the given tensor.   We write, then,

25.4 $\phi_{i,j} = \partial_j \phi_i - \Gamma_{ij}^k \phi_k,$

so that $d\phi_i v^i = \phi_{i,j} v^i dx^j$.

Exercise 1.   Apply the method leading to this formula to a tensor field of rank
two and derive the formula for the covariant derivatives in this case.
Exercise 2.   Find the covariant derivatives of the tensor g_{ij}.

In order to be able to perform algebraic operations on vectors and
tensors—addition, multiplication, contraction—the values of the g's

must be given.   In order to be able to perform the operation of differentiation the Γ's must be known also.   However, if the g's are known at all the points of the space (or at least in a neighborhood of the point considered), the Γ's can be found.   Differentiation of formula (24.2) $g_{ij} = \mathbf{c}_i\mathbf{c}_j$ which defined the g's yields

$$\partial_k g_{ij} = (\partial_k \mathbf{c}_i) \cdot \mathbf{c}_j + \mathbf{c}_i \cdot \partial_k \mathbf{c}_j,$$

which, by the substitution of the expression 25.3 for the derivatives of the $\mathbf{c}$'s, becomes

$$\partial_k g_{ij} = \Gamma^s_{ki}\mathbf{c}_s\mathbf{c}_j + \mathbf{c}_i\Gamma^s_{kj}\mathbf{c}_s,$$

or, finally, by 24.2,

25.5 $$\partial_k g_{ij} = g_{sj}\Gamma^s_{ki} + g_{is}\Gamma^s_{kj}.$$

These equations establish the relation between the g's and the Γ's. They must be solved for the Γ's.   In order to do this, notice that the Γ's are symmetric with respect to their lower indices; i.e.,

25.51 $$\Gamma^s_{ki} = \Gamma^s_{ik}.$$

In fact, $\partial_k \mathbf{c}_i = \partial_k\partial_i P$, and this, if the derivatives are assumed to be continuous, is equal to $\partial_i\partial_k P$, so that $\partial_k \mathbf{c}_i = \partial_i \mathbf{c}_k$, which, with 25.3, proves 25.51.   This relation 25.51 reduces the number of unknowns (the Γ's) in 25.5 to the number of equations and makes the solution possible.   The solution is accomplished by interchanging i and k and then j and k in 25.5 to obtain, first of all,

$$\partial_i g_{kj} = g_{sj}\Gamma^s_{ik} + g_{ks}\Gamma^s_{ii} \quad \text{and} \quad \partial_j g_{ik} = g_{sk}\Gamma^s_{ji} + g_{is}\Gamma^s_{jk}.$$

If equation 25.5 is subtracted from the sum of the last two equations and 25.51 is used, one obtains

25.52 $$g_{ks}\Gamma^s_{ij} = \tfrac{1}{2}(\partial_i g_{kj} + \partial_j g_{ik} - \partial_k g_{ij}) \equiv \Gamma_{k;ij},$$

where the Γ with three subscripts is just a convenient notation for the middle term.   The $\Gamma_{k;ij}$ can be calculated when the g's are given as functions of the coordinates, so that the Γ^s_{ij} which are needed can be found by multiplying all members of 25.52 by g^{mk} (this implies contraction with respect to k).   Using the relation $g^{mk}g_{ks} = \delta_{ms}$, one finds

25.53 $$\Gamma^m_{ij} = \tfrac{1}{2}g^{mk}(\partial_i g_{ks} + \partial_j g_{ik} - \partial_k g_{ij}) = g^{mk}\Gamma_{k;ij}.$$

REMARK.   The quantities Γ^m_{ij} and $\Gamma_{k;ij}$ were introduced by Christoffel and are sometimes known as the Christoffel symbols with three indices.   It is worth noting that they are *not* the components of a tensor; in fact, if they were, the tensor would be $\Gamma_{ij}^k x^i y^j z_k$. But when the $\mathbf{c}$'s are constant vectors (as they are in cartesian coordinates) the Γ's are zero so that the value of this "tensor" is zero in that system of coordinates while it is obviously different from zero in other systems. This is a contradiction, since a tensor is independent of its representations.

Exercise 3. Prove that in n-dimensional space there are $\dfrac{n^2(n+1)}{2}$ different Γ's.

Exercise 4. Prove that for cartesian coordinates the Γ's are zero.

In arriving at formula 25.4 it was assumed that the tensor was given by its covariant components. When it is given by its contravariant components ϕ^i, it is convenient to consider it as an inner product, and to write $\phi(\mathbf{u}) = \mathbf{v} \cdot \mathbf{u}$, where $\mathbf{v}$ is the vector whose components are ϕ^i and $\mathbf{u}$ is the vector argument (compare statement after 24.21). Then

25.6 $$d\phi(\mathbf{u}) = d(\mathbf{v} \cdot \mathbf{u}) = (\partial_j \mathbf{v} \cdot \mathbf{u}) \cdot dx^j,$$

since $\mathbf{u}$ is supposed to be kept constant during the differentiation. Now, $\mathbf{v} = \mathbf{c}_i \phi^i$, so that $\partial_j \mathbf{v} = (\partial_j \mathbf{c}_i)\phi^i + \mathbf{c}_i \cdot \partial_j \phi^i$. If the expressions 25.3 are substituted for $\partial_j c_i$ and the summation index changed, this becomes

$$\partial_j \mathbf{v} = (\Gamma_{kj}^i \phi^k + \partial_j \phi^i)\mathbf{c}_i.$$

The substitution of this into 25.6, with the fact that (see 24.22) $\mathbf{c}_i \mathbf{u} = u_i$, implies that

$$d\phi(\mathbf{u}) = (\partial_j \phi^i + \Gamma_{kj}^i \phi^k)u_i \cdot dx^j.$$

This shows that the quantities

$$\partial_j \phi^i + \Gamma_{kj}^i \phi^k$$

are the mixed components of the differential of ϕ. This is similar to the situation in the discussion which led to 25.33 in that the components of the differential of a tensor (given by its contravariant components) are not the derivatives of these components but require a correction. As there, these expressions are called the covariant derivatives but, it is necessary to add, of the contravariant components of ϕ. They are denoted by $\phi^i{}_{,j}$, so that

25.7 $$\phi^i{}_{,j} = \partial_j \phi^i + \Gamma_{kj}^i \phi^k.$$

The comma which must precede the index accruing from differentiation should not be placed under the superscript i, but an empty space should be left there in case it is necessary to lower an index.

The same tensor may be given by its covariant or by its contravariant components. We have determined the procedure for obtaining the covariant and the mixed components of the differential. Of course, these two types of components also give different representations of the *same* tensor, and one representation can be obtained from another by the raising or lowering of the indices, so that, for example,

$$g^{ik}\phi_{i,j} = \phi^k{}_{,j}.$$

Exercise 5.   Prove this relation by computation.

To obtain the components of the differential of a tensor of higher rank the same procedure could be used as for tensors of rank one. However, it is more convenient to use the fact that a tensor of rank r is a sum of products of tensors of rank one as well as the following properties of the differential of the sum and product

1. $d(\phi + \psi) = d\phi + d\psi$ (additivity).

2. $d(\phi \cdot \psi) = d\phi \cdot \psi + \phi \cdot d\psi.$

(Analogous relations hold for three or more functions.)

From this it may be concluded that if $\omega_{ij} = \Sigma \phi_i \psi_j$ then $\omega_{ij,k} = \Sigma(\phi_{i,k}\psi_j + \phi_i \psi_{j,k})$. The replacement of $\phi_{i,k}$ and $\phi_{j,k}$ by their expressions as given by 25.4 yields

$$\omega_{ij,k} = \Sigma(\partial_k \phi_i)\psi_j - \Sigma\Gamma^s_{ki}\phi_s\psi_j + \Sigma\phi_i\partial_k\psi_j - \Sigma\phi_i\Gamma^s_{kj}\psi_s$$

$$= \Sigma((\partial_k\phi_i)\psi_j + \phi_i(\partial_k\psi_j)) - \Gamma^s_{ki}\Sigma\phi_s\psi_j - \Gamma^s_{kj}\phi_i\psi_s.$$

Since the first summation is simply $\partial_k\omega_{ij}$ (by the rule of differentiation of a product) this reduces to

25.71 $$\omega_{ij,k} = \partial_k\omega_{ij} - \Gamma^s_{ki}\omega_{sj} - \Gamma^s_{kj}\omega_{is}.$$

In a similar way, by using 25.7 for one of the factors, one has

25.72 $$\omega^i{}_{j,k} = \partial_k\omega^i{}_j + \Gamma^i_{sk}\omega^s{}_j - \Gamma^s_{kj}\omega^i{}_s$$

and similar formulas for covariant derivatives of any tensor. These formulas are easily remembered if a tensor with any number of indices is thought of as a product of factors each of which carries only one of the indices.

26. General coordinates in curved spaces

We introduced curved spaces in the early sections of this chapter and succeeded in characterizing curvature by certain tensors. It was found later (section 23) that in order to discuss differentiation of such tensors a coordinate system covering the whole (or at least a whole portion) of a curved space was needed. The technique of representing tensors in such a general coordinate system was developed. This technique was extended to include differentiation but only for flat spaces. It was not necessary to introduce a new operation, but merely to express a known operation in a new way. Now it will be necessary to define new operations, but it will be shown that this can be done in such a way that the technique of section 25 will not have to be changed at all.

As far as differentiation of a tensor field of rank zero—a scalar field —is concerned, there is nothing new to be said when the transition from flat to curved space is made. The differential is again a tensor field of rank one given by the same formula $df = \partial_i f \cdot dx^i$, and the dx^i may be considered the components of a vector $dP = c_i \, dx^i$. This vector is, of course, tangent to the curved space at the point P. More generally, the vectors that appear as arguments of tensors, whether they have been obtained by differentiation of tensors of lower rank, or not, are vectors of the flat space tangent at a point P to a curved space C (which for purposes of visualization may be thought of as a surface). The initial point of the vector may be placed at the point of contact P. A tensor at P is a (multilinear) function of vectors at P, and a tensor field is said to be given when a tensor is defined at every point of C (or of a part of it). Such a tensor field of rank r is a function of $r + 1$ arguments. It depends on the point P and on the values of r vector arguments, but it is a function of a peculiar kind in that the domain of the vector variables is itself variable: when another point P is considered the vector arguments must be chosen from the vectors of the flat tangent at the new point. Of course, this means that the coordinate vectors, the c_i, will change from point to point. This fact, that the c's change from point to point, is nothing new, since the change of the c's has already been considered in flat space when general coordinates were introduced. Here, however, the change is, so to say, more radical in that, whereas there the derivatives of the c's could be expressed as linear combinations of the c's themselves, this is not true here. However, $\partial_j c_i$ is for every j and i a vector of the N-dimensional flat containing C, and it may be considered as decomposed into tangential and normal components, belonging to the tangential n-dimensional flat, and to the r-dimensional normal space, respectively (compare definitions following 21.71). The tangential components of $\partial_j c_i$ can, as the whole vector could before, be presented as $\Gamma_{ij}^k c_k$, so that

26.1 $$\partial_j c_i = \Gamma_{ij}^k c_k + n_{ij},$$

where n_{ij} is a normal vector. The important fact is that this additional term does not affect the derivatives of g_{ij}. In fact, repeating the calculation leading to formula 25.5 we have here

$$\partial_k(c_i c_j) = (\partial_k c_i) \cdot c_j + c_i \cdot \partial_k c_j$$

$$= \Gamma_{ik}^s c_s c_j + n_{ik} c_j + c_i \cdot \Gamma_{jk}^s c_s + c_i n_{jk}.$$

The two terms involving normal vectors disappear because these normal vectors are multiplied by tangent vectors which are by definition perpendicular to them. Thus formula 25.5 remains applicable, as well as the expression for the Γ's in terms of the derivatives of the g's.

We consider next the differentiation of a vector. As before, set $\mathbf{v} = v^i c_i$ and

$$\partial_j \mathbf{v} = \partial_j v^i \cdot c_i + v^i \partial_j c_i.$$

Now, since $\partial_j c_i$ has an extra term, so does $\partial_j \mathbf{v}$; namely,

26.11 $$\partial_j \mathbf{v} = (\partial_j v^k + \Gamma_{ij}^k v^i) c_k + v^i n_{ij}.$$

In the case of flat space we used the vanishing of $\partial_j \mathbf{v}^k + \Gamma_{ij}^k v^i$ as the condition of constancy of the vector field. Here

26.2 $$\partial_j v^k + \Gamma_{ij}^k v^i = 0 \quad \text{or} \quad \partial_j v^k = -\Gamma_{ij}^k v^i$$

means only that the *tangential component* of the change is zero, or that the change of the vector is entirely in normal directions. We may say that a vector field is *relatively constant* at a point if the tangential components of its derivatives are zero at that point.

REMARK. Using a terminology familiar in other branches of mathematics we could say also that the vector field is constant at the point P *modulo the normal space*.

We used the concept of a constant field to define differentiation of tensors in flat space. To obtain the differential of a tensor field of rank r we had to go through three stages. In the first, the vector arguments were thought of as belonging to constant fields. In the second, the resulting quantity was differentiated as a function of coordinates. Finally, in the third, variability was restored to the vector arguments. Our definition of differentiation for a curved space will be the same, except that *relative* constancy will replace constancy.

DEFINITION. By the differential at P of a tensor field of rank r we shall mean the tensor of rank $r + 1$ obtained by first substituting for the vector arguments vectors belonging to fields relatively constant at P, then differentiating the resulting function, and finally (observing that the results depends only on the values at P of these relatively constant fields) considering these values as variable.

With this definition, which incidentally is independent of the coordinate system since relative constancy was defined geometrically, *all the calculations leading to various formulas of the preceding section remain applicable to tensor fields of curved space.*

The differential so obtained is sometimes called the *absolute* differential (although relative differential might be a more appropriate name). The components of the differential are called the covariant derivatives of the components of the given tensor field.

In applying the preceding formulas to special cases we begin with the calculation of the $\mathbf{c}$'s. If the surface is given by expressing the coordinates X^1, X^2, X^3 of its points in the flat space containing it as functions of the general coordinates of the surface, x^1, x^2, the components of the $\mathbf{c}$'s considered as vectors of the space will be

$$\mathbf{c}_1 = (\partial_1 X^1, \partial_1 X^2, \partial_1 X^3), \qquad \mathbf{c}_2 = (\partial_2 X^1, \partial_2 X^2, \partial_2 X^3);$$

from these the g's are obtained as

$$g_{11} = (\partial_1 X^1)^2 + (\partial_1 X^2)^2 + (\partial_1 X^3)^2,$$

$$g_{12} = \partial_1 X^1 \cdot \partial_2 X^1 + \partial_1 X^2 \cdot \partial_2 X^2 + \partial_1 X^3 \cdot \partial_2 X^3,$$

$$g_{22} = (\partial_2 X^1)^2 + (\partial_2 X^2)^2 + (\partial_2 X^3)^2.$$

In the general case of a curved n-space in flat N-space,

26.4 $\mathbf{c}_i = (\partial_i X^h)$ $(h = 1, \cdots N; i = 1, \cdots, n)$

and

26.41 $$g_{ij} = \sum_{h=1}^{N} (\partial_i X^h) \cdot (\partial_j X^h).$$

Exercise. Consider the surface of a sphere given parametrically by $P = (r \cos x^1 \cdot \cos x^2, r \cos x^1 \cdot \sin x^2, r \sin x^1)$; find $\mathbf{c}_1$, $\mathbf{c}_2$, g_{ij}, g^{ij}, and the Γ's.

In the early sections of this chapter curved surfaces and spaces have been studied by using the cartesian coordinates of the flat space of higher dimensions in which they are located. In section 23 it was indicated how the cartesian coordinates on the tangent plane can be used as coordinates for the points of the surface (or curved space). The use of these coordinates, which we shall refer to as *quasi-cartesian* coordinates, often simplifies calculations; we shall apply now the preceding technique to these coordinates.

If quasi-cartesian coordinates are used, the first n coordinates of the imbedding space serve as the general coordinates of C. Dividing the sum in the expression for g_{ij} into two parts we can write

26.42 $$g_{ij} = \sum_{h=1}^{n} (\partial_i x^h)(\partial_j x^h) + \sum_{k=1}^{r} (\partial_i x^{n+k})(\partial_j x^{n+k}).$$

The first summation is, so to say, in C, and the summation convention concerning repeated indices can be used. Moreover, $\partial_i x^h = \delta_{ih}$, so that the first sum in the above expression reduces to δ_{ij}. For x^{n+k} we use formulas 21.71, which with the indices in the proper places give

$$x^{n+k} = \tfrac{1}{2}a_{ij}^{(k)}x^i x^j + \text{terms of higher degree.}$$

Thus

$$\partial_s x^{n+k} = \tfrac{1}{2}a_{ij}^{(k)}(\partial_s x^i)\cdot x^j + \tfrac{1}{2}a_{ij}^{(k)}x^i(\partial_s x^j) + \text{t.h.d.}$$

$$= \tfrac{1}{2}a_{ij}^{(k)}\delta_{si}x^j + \tfrac{1}{2}a_{ij}^{(k)}x^i\delta_{sj} + \text{t.h.d.}$$

$$= a_{is}^{(k)}x^i + \text{t.h.d.,}$$

so that substitution into 26.42 yields

26.43 $$g_{ij} = \delta_{ij} + \sum_{k=1}^{r} a_{si}^{(k)}x^s \cdot a_{mj}^{(k)}x^m + \text{t.h.d.}$$

These formulas give the values for the g's in quasi-cartesian coordinates for a neighborhood of the point of contact. For the point of contact itself, i.e., for the origin of the coordinates,

26.5 $$(g_{ij})_0 = \delta_{ij}$$

and, of course, also

26.51 $$(g^{ij})_0 = \delta_{ij}.$$

As a consequence of this the distinction between covariant and contravariant components vanishes for quasi-cartesian coordinates at the point of contact.

The differentiation of 26.43 shows that the series for the derivatives of the g's contain no constant terms so that at the point of contact these derivatives are zero. This holds for the Γ's also in view of their expression (25.53) in terms of the derivatives. For future reference this will be noted by writing

26.52 $$(\Gamma_{ij}^k)_0 = 0.$$

The point of contact, or the origin, in quasi-cartesian coordinates is a place where the situation is the closest possible to that which exists in flat space when cartesian coordinates are used. However, the second derivatives of the g's do not, in general, vanish at the origin. Two differentiations and setting $x^i = 0$ yields the following formula for these second derivatives:

$$26.6 \qquad (\partial_h \partial_p g_{ij})_0 = \sum_{k=1}^{r} (a_{pi}^{(k)} a_{hj}^{(k)} + a_{hi}^{(k)} a_{pj}^{(k)}).$$

This will be used in the next section.

If a curved n-space is given by equations expressing the coordinates of a flat N-space in terms of n parameters (which serve as coordinates of the curved space) we know how to find the g's. The question now arises: if we are given $\frac{1}{2}n(n + 1)$ functions of the coordinates, is it possible to find a space for which these functions serve as the g's? This question reduces to solving the system of partial differential equations 26.41, and without going into details we shall state that such a system of equations, in general, can be solved if the number of unknown functions is equal to that of equations. Since there are $\frac{1}{2}n(n + 1)$ equations here, there must be that many unknown functions. This means that the number of dimensions N of the containing space must be $\frac{1}{2}n(n + 1)$ in general. In special cases it may, of course, be less than that. We may say then: a two-dimensional curved space given by its g's may be always considered as immersed into a three-dimensional space, a three-dimensional curved space may be always considered as part of a six-dimensional flat space, and a four-dimensional as part of a ten-dimensional flat.

REMARK. The above statement that, given $\frac{1}{2}n(n + 1)$ functions, it is possible to interpret them as the g's of a curved space, which is part of a flat space of that number of dimensions, is not necessarily true for the whole space; it applies for a suitably chosen neighborhood of every point.

Another question is whether, for a given set of *real* g's, the containing space will come out *real?* This is by no means always so. For example, for $g_{11} = g_{22} = g_{33} = -g_{44} = 1$, and all other $g_{ij} = 0$, the minimum cartesian containing space is four-dimensional with one imaginary coordinate, and it is clear that no real cartesian space can contain it.

Henceforth we may consider the curved space as given by its g's, and the g's may be considered as arbitrarily given functions of the x's.

It may seem that the original purpose of introducing curved space, which was to obtain a tensor that we could identify with T_{ij}, has been lost sight of.   The Riemann tensor was introduced with this in mind, but now we seem to be immersed in an entirely formal theory which is far removed from the Riemann tensor.   As a matter of fact, it is just around the corner.   Indeed, differentiation, although performed according to formulas that are formally the same as in flat space, has, as we shall see, a new content.   In trying to discover the difference we will be led to the Riemann tensor from a new point of view.

27. Riemann tensor in general coordinates

We said that the meaning of differentiation in curved space is different from that in flat space.   To demonstrate this difference in one important aspect consider a tensor of the first rank given in its contravariant components F^i.   It may be differentiated twice to give a tensor of third rank $F^i{}_{,jk}$.   In flat space this tensor would not differ from $F^i{}_{,kj}$ because in cartesian components differentiation of a tensor reduces to ordinary differentiation of its components.   That is, the cartesian components of the two tensors mentioned are $\partial_k\partial_j F^i$ and $\partial_j\partial_k F^i$, respectively, and these are equal because the result of *ordinary* differentiation does not depend on the order.   Two tensors with equal components in one system of coordinates would be equal in all systems of coordinates so that

27.1 $$F^i{}_{,jk} - F^i{}_{,kj} = 0 \quad \text{in flat space.}$$

This reasoning does not apply in curved space because there are no cartesian coordinates there.   The question of whether $F^i{}_{,jk}$ is equal to $F^i{}_{,kj}$ is still open and must be settled by direct computation.

Consider the contravariant components F^i, and calculate components of the first differential according to formula 25.7 to obtain

27.2 $$F^i{}_{,j} = \partial_j F^i + \Gamma^i_{sj} F^s.$$

Next, differentiate this again to obtain, according to formula 25.72,

27.21 $$F^i{}_{,jk} = \partial_k F^i{}_{,j} + \Gamma^i_{sk} F^s{}_{,j} - \Gamma^m_{jk} F^i{}_{,m}.$$

Now form the difference to be investigated, viz.,

$$F^i{}_{,jk} - F^i{}_{,kj} = \partial_k F^i{}_{,j} - \partial_j F^i{}_{,k} + \Gamma^i_{mk} F^m{}_{,j} - \Gamma^i_{mj} F^m{}_{,k} - (\Gamma^m_{jk} - \Gamma^m_{kj}) F^i{}_{,m}.$$

The last parenthesis vanishes according to 25.51, and the remainder reduces, after the substitution of the above expression 27.2 for the first derivative and rearrangement of terms, to

$$\partial_k\partial_j F^i - \partial_j\partial_k F^i + \Gamma^i_{sj}\partial_k F^s - \Gamma^i_{mj}\partial_k F^m + \Gamma^i_{mk}\partial_j F^m - \Gamma^i_{sk}\partial_j F^s$$
$$+ (\partial_k\Gamma^i_{js} - \partial_j\Gamma^i_{ks} + \Gamma^i_{mk}\Gamma^m_{sj} - \Gamma^i_{mj}\Gamma^m_{sk})F^s.$$

Here cancellation takes place in the first three pairs of terms; in the first, as a result of independence of ordinary differentiation on order, and in the next two pairs as a result of the fact that the name of the index of summation is immaterial. Thus

27.3 $\quad F^i_{,jk} - F^i_{,kj} = (\partial_k\Gamma^i_{sj} - \partial_j\Gamma^i_{sk} + \Gamma^i_{mk}\Gamma^m_{sj} - \Gamma^i_{mj}\Gamma^m_{sk})F^s$

or

27.4 $\qquad\qquad\qquad F^i_{,jk} - F^i_{,kj} = B^i_{s,jk}F^s$

where

27.5 $\qquad\quad B^i_{s,jk} = \partial_k\Gamma^i_{sj} - \partial_j\Gamma^i_{sk} + \Gamma^i_{mk}\Gamma^m_{sj} - \Gamma^i_{mj}\Gamma^m_{sk}.$

Before discussing the question of whether the expression vanishes or not, it will be shown that the B's are the components of a tensor. In fact, multiplying both sides of 27.4 by $x_i y^j z^s$, where x_i, y^j, z^s are components of arbitrary vectors, and contracting, we have

$$(F^i_{,jk} - F^i_{,kj})x_i y^j z^k = B^i_{s,jk}x_i F^s y^j z^k.$$

The left-hand side is the difference of two tensors and therefore is a tensor. Therefore the right-hand side is also a tensor and the B's are tensor components. (We saw in section 25, in the example of the Γ's, that not every symbol with indices may be interpreted as a component of a tensor—that is why it was important to show that the B's are tensor components.)

The question as to the vanishing of 27.3 can be settled by showing that the B's are mixed components of the Riemann tensor that was introduced in section 22. Since it has been proved that they are components of a tensor, any system of coordinates, in particular a quasi-cartesian system, can be employed. In such a system the Γ's vanish at the point of contact (26.52) so that only the terms

27.6 $\qquad\qquad\qquad \partial_k\Gamma^i_{sj} - \partial_j\Gamma^i_{sk}$

remain.

If the Γ's with one upper index are replaced by their expressions in terms of the g's with upper indices and the Γ's with all indices down (formula 25.53), we obtain

$$(\partial_k g^{im})\Gamma_{m;sj} - (\partial_j g^{im})\Gamma_{m;sk} + g^{im}\partial_k\Gamma_{m;sj} - g^{im}\partial_j\Gamma_{m;sk}.$$

The first two terms vanish again because the Γ's vanish at the point of contact. If the fact that the g's are equal to the δ's at the point of contact, and the expressions 25.52 are used, the above reduces, after a few cancellations, to

$$B_{is;jk} = \tfrac{1}{2}(\partial_k\partial_s g_{ij} - \partial_k\partial_i g_{sj} - \partial_j\partial_s g_{ik} + \partial_j\partial_i g_{sk}).$$

If the expressions 26.6 are used for the second derivatives of the g's, this can be written

27.7 $$B_{is;jm} = \Sigma(a_{ij}^{(k)}a_{sm}^{(k)} - a_{im}^{(k)}a_{sj}^{(k)}).$$

The comparison of this with the expression for the Riemann tensor deduced at the end of section 22 demonstrates the identity of the two expressions except for the use of different letters as subscripts.

This shows that, if the Riemann tensor does not vanish, the second differential of a vector field actually may depend on the order of differentiation. This fact is very interesting in itself. It confirms the statement that in curved space differentiation has a new meaning, and it has many important implications, on which, however, we cannot dwell here. For us it is important that we have obtained an expression of the Riemann tensor in terms of the g's alone. This means that those properties of the curvature of space which are expressed in the Riemann tensor are determined by the *metric* of the space; i.e., if distances along different curves are given, the curvature (as far as it is expressed in the Riemann tensor) is determined. According to our conception, the inhabitants of the space certainly can measure lengths. It follows that curvature, as expressed by the Riemann tensor, is accessible to the inhabitants, and that it is an internal property of the space. In particular, for $N = 3$, $n = 2$, i.e., for the ordinary surface, this proves, as promised in section 20, that the total curvature can be calculated from the expression for the line element. This is Gauss's theorema egregium.

REMARK. The property of relative constancy of a vector field as defined in section 26 is a local property since we defined relative constancy *at a point*. The question may arise: are there vector fields that are relatively constant at every point of the region in which they are defined? To find such a field, if one exists, it would be necessary to integrate the system of differential equations 26.2

$$\partial_j v^i = -\Gamma_{jk}^i v^k.$$

Differentiating this and substituting for the derivative on the right gives

$$\partial_s\partial_j v^i = -(\partial_s\Gamma_{jm}^i)v^m + \Gamma_{jk}^i\Gamma_{sm}^k v^m.$$

Assuming that it is permissible to interchange the order of ordinary differentiation, one obtains

$$(-\partial_s\Gamma^i_{jm} + \partial_j\Gamma^i_{sm} + \Gamma^i_{jk}\Gamma^k_{sm} - \Gamma^i_{sk}\Gamma^k_{jm})v^m = 0.$$

The comparison of this with 27.5 shows that the expressions in parentheses are the components of the Riemann tensor so that the existence of vector fields relatively constant at every point depends on the vanishing of the Riemann tensor.

The method of quasi-cartesian coordinates in proving a relation between tensors that was used in identifying the B's with the components of the Riemann tensor can be applied often and helps to avoid lengthy computations. We shall use it now to prove certain differential relations for the Riemann tensor that are very important for us because we know that the tensor $T^i{}_j$, which we want to identify with the contracted Riemann tensor, satisfies a certain differential equation, namely, $\partial_j T^j{}_i = 0$. Of course, we expect that the tensor in our mathematical theory with which we are going to identify T satisfies the same relations. In order to deduce differential relations on the contracted Riemann tensor it is necessary to prove first some relations for the non-contracted tensor. These relations were discovered by Ricci and then rediscovered by Bianchi and bear Bianchi's name. They are

27.8 $R^i{}_{j;mn,p} + R^i{}_{j;np,m} + R^i{}_{j;pm,n} = 0.$

The proof is very simple if quasi-cartesian coordinates are used. In these coordinates the Γ's at the point of contact vanish, and, although the first derivatives of the Γ's do not, the components of the tensor obtained by differentiating the B's (formula 27.5) which were identified with the R's will contain the second derivatives only, because the first derivatives will be multiplied by the Γ's themselves, and these do vanish. With this in mind the proof of the Bianchi relations does not present any difficulty. One simply substitutes the difference of the two second-order derivatives for each of the three terms in 27.8 and finds that the result vanishes identically.

Now, in order to deduce the relations for the contracted tensor from 27.8, raise the second index in the terms of that formula, so that it becomes

$$R^{ij}{}_{mn,p} + R^{ij}{}_{np,m} + R^{ij}{}_{pm,n} = 0,$$

and then contract i with m, and j with n, to obtain

$$R^{ij}{}_{ij,p} + R^{ij}{}_{jp,i} + R^{ij}{}_{pi,j} = 0.$$

The second term here may be written as $-R^{ji}{}_{jp,i}$ if the fact (compare 22.71) that the Riemann tensor changes its sign when two indices of the same pair are interchanged is used. Now, the third term is equal to the second, as can be seen by interchanging i and j (which does not change the value of the expression since i and j are summation indices), and then interchanging the indices in each pair (which changes the sign twice). Thus

$$R^{ij}{}_{ij,p} - 2R^{ij}{}_{pj,i} = 0.$$

But $R^{ij}{}_{pj}$ are the mixed components of the contracted Riemann tensor which was denoted by $R^i{}_p$, so that, dividing by 2 and changing the sign, we have

$$R^i{}_{p,i} - \tfrac{1}{2}R^i{}_{i,p} = 0.$$

Finally, $R^i{}_i$ is the result of a contraction of the contracted Riemann tensor. Denote this scalar, or tensor of rank zero, by R (it is called the twice-contracted Riemann tensor). Then we can write simply $R_{,p}$ or $(\delta_{ip}R)_{,i}$ for $R^i{}_{i,p}$ and the above relation becomes

27.9 $$(R^i{}_p - \tfrac{1}{2}\delta_{ip}R)_{,i} = 0.$$

28. Geodesics

In concluding this fragmentary development of the mathematical theory which will be applied to physics in the next chapter we shall study a class of curves in curved space which play an important part in the discussion of motion. These curves may be considered generalizations of straight lines in flat space, and we shall begin by considering these.

Consider a straight line as a special case of a curve in parametric form; i.e., consider the coordinates x^i as functions of a parameter p. When cartesian coordinates are used the parametric formulas are, as we know (compare 7.11),

$$x^i = a^i + pv^i,$$

where the a's and the v's are constants. The components of a tangent vector to the curve (compare section 13) are given by dx^i/dp, which here are equal to v^i. This vector must therefore be considered a tangent vector, and it is the same for all points of the curve. (The same locus can be represented, of course, in terms of some other parameter q, and then dx^i/dq will not necessarily be the same vector for all points.) We are thus led to the characterization of a straight line as a one-parameter locus such that the vector dx^i/dp is constant for some choices of the parameter. This, of course, is independent of the system of coordinates, although in a general coordinate system the constant vector will not have constant components.   If in general coordinates dx^i/dp is again denoted by v^i the constancy of the vector will be expressed by $d(v^i \mathbf{c}_i)/dp = 0$ or by

$$\frac{dv^i}{dp} \mathbf{c}_i + v^i \frac{d\mathbf{c}_i}{dp} = 0.$$

Since the $\mathbf{c}$'s depend on p through the coordinates we will have $d\mathbf{c}_i/dp = \partial_j \mathbf{c}_i \cdot dx^j/dp = \partial_j \mathbf{c}_i \cdot v^j$.   By substituting from 25.3, changing the summation index, and making use of the independence of the $\mathbf{c}$'s (compare the discussion leading to the constancy condition 25.31) this may be written

$$\frac{dv^i}{dp} + v^j \Gamma^i_{jk} v^k = 0$$

or

28.1 $$\frac{d^2 x^i}{dp^2} + \Gamma^i_{jk} \frac{dx^j}{dp} \frac{dx^k}{dp} = 0.$$

In words: a necessary and sufficient condition for a one-parameter locus to represent a straight line is the existence of a parametrization for which 28.1 is satisfied.

The reader may have noticed the similarity of this derivation with that for the equation of a constant vector field given in section 25. We may say that we have here a one-dimensional constant field of vectors (tangent vectors to the curve, or rather equal vectors in different points of a straight line).

We found in section 26 that our formulas in general coordinates which were first derived for flat space possessed some meaning in curved space also, although not necessarily the same meaning.   A similar thing happens with the equation of a straight line.   In curved space the condition of constancy of the vector of components $v^i = dx^i/dp$ means of course only *relative* constancy; i.e., it means that the tangential component of the change of $\mathbf{v}$ are zero.   This leads us to adopt the following definition: a curve $x^i(p)$ will be called a *geodesic* if for a proper choice of parameter the vectors of components dx^i/dp constitute a (one-dimensional) field which is relatively constant at every point.

With this definition we can state that a necessary and sufficient condition for a curve to be a geodesic is that for a proper choice of the parameter it satisfy equation 28.1.   Differentiation with respect to such a parameter will be denoted by a dot placed above the letter.

There is a certain freedom in choosing the parameter for which equations 28.1 are satisfied. If, instead of p, a new parameter q is chosen, it follows that

$$\frac{dx^i}{dp} = \frac{dx^i}{dq}\frac{dq}{dp}; \quad \frac{d^2x^i}{dp^2} = \frac{d^2x^i}{dq^2}\left(\frac{dq}{dp}\right)^2 + \frac{dx^i}{dq}\frac{d^2q}{dp^2}.$$

Equations 28.1 now become

$$\left(\frac{d^2x^i}{dq^2} + \Gamma^i_{jk}\frac{dx^j}{dq}\frac{dx^k}{dq}\right)\left(\frac{dq}{dp}\right)^2 + \frac{dx^i}{dq}\frac{d^2q}{dp^2} = 0.$$

We see that these equations have the form 28.1 if and only if $d^2q/dp^2 = 0$; i.e., the permissible changes of parameter are given by

$$q = ap + b,$$

where a and b are constants.

Let us consider the tangent vectors dx^i/dp to a geodesic in more detail (we assume that p is one of the parameters for which 28.1 hold). We know that this field is relatively constant at every. point. We want to prove now that all the vectors have the same length. The square of the length of this vector is $g_{ij}\dfrac{dx^i}{dp}\dfrac{dx^j}{dp}$. Differentiating this we obtain, using 28.1,

$$\frac{d}{dp}\left(g_{ij}\frac{dx^i}{dp}\frac{dx^j}{dp}\right) = \frac{dg_{ij}}{dp}\frac{dx^i}{dp}\frac{dx^j}{dp} + g_{ij}\frac{d^2x^i}{dp^2}\frac{dx^j}{dp} + g_{ij}\frac{dx^i}{dp}\frac{d^2x^j}{dp^2}$$

$$= \partial_k g_{ij}\frac{dx^k}{dp}\frac{dx^i}{dp}\frac{dx^j}{dp} - g_{ij}\Gamma^i_{ks}\frac{dx^k}{dp}\frac{dx^s}{dp}\frac{dx^j}{dp} - g_{ij}\frac{dx^i}{dp}\Gamma^j_{ks}\frac{dx^k}{dp}\frac{dx^s}{dp}.$$

Changing the summation indices this may be written

$$(\partial_k g_{ij} - g_{sj}\Gamma^s_{ki} - g_{is}\Gamma^s_{kj})\frac{dx^k}{dp}\frac{dx^i}{dp}\frac{dx^j}{dp},$$

and this is zero according to 25.5. We see thus that the square of the vector dx^i/dp is constant along the geodesic. If it is not zero it may be made into a unit vector so that p is arc length. We see, then, that if the tangent vectors along a geodesic are *not of zero square* we can use arc length (or any linear function of it) as a parameter in equation 28.1. But the case when the tangent vectors are of zero square is also important (the curves in this case represent motion of photons).

Our discussion has been general enough to include this since we have avoided making $p = s$ throughout.

REMARK. Often geodesics are defined as the *shortest* lines on a surface (or in a curved space) and are introduced by means of calculus of variations. Since lengths in the time-space of relativity can be represented by zero and imaginary numbers as well as positive numbers this way of discussing geodesics becomes more complicated. Instead we could say that geodesics, as we have introduced them, are *straightest* lines. A straight line is a line that does not change its direction, i.e., a line along which a unit vector does not change. Since this is impossible on a curved surface, it is necessary to introduce "straightest lines," i.e., lines that change their direction "as little as possible." Now the unit vector must change from point to point because the tangent plane to which it belongs changes. The derivative cannot be zero because its normal component cannot be zero; so the best we can hope for is for its tangential component to be zero, and that is what the above equation expresses.

In general, we know that curves in space-time represent motions. A curve represents the motion of a single particle. If we consider continuous distribution of matter we have a *family* of curves such that there is one and only one curve through every point (of the region of space-time we are considering). In every point of that region we may consider a tangent vector $v^i = dx^i/dp$ of the curve passing through that point. If the curves of the family are geodesics we will choose the parameter on every curve in such a way that we can use equations 28.1. These parameters having been chosen, the tangent vectors will be determined and we will have a vector field—which we may call a geodesic vector field. It should be emphasized that the field is not entirely determined by the geodesics in the sense that specific parametrizations of the curves must also be chosen, and changing the parametrizations leads to another geodesic field for the same family of geodesics.

The components v^i are now functions of the coordinates. The parametrizations on different curves are of course independent of each other, but we will assume that it was possible to choose them (and still have equations 28.1 satisfied) in such a way that the v^i are differentiable functions of the coordinates.

If that is so, we can express the condition of relative constancy of the vector along the curve by saying that the tangential components of

$$\frac{d\mathbf{v}}{dp} = \partial_j \mathbf{v} \frac{dx^j}{dp} = \partial_j \mathbf{v} \, v^j$$

must vanish.   But (compare 26.11)

$$\partial_j \mathbf{v} = (\partial_j v^i + \Gamma^i_{jk} v^k)\mathbf{c}_i + v^i \mathbf{n}_{ij}$$

so that the condition is

28.2 $$v^i,_j v^j = 0.$$

We can say that this is the condition for a vector field to be geodesic.

29. Equations of physics in general coordinates

When we wrote the equations of physics (for instance, in section 12) we used flat space and cartesian coordinates one of which was imaginary.   Now that we have introduced general coordinates and curved space we want to see how these changes affect our equations.

As a first step we want to see how the introduction of covariant and contravariant components will affect the equations.   We will use the physical coordinates x, y, z, and t to represent points and the ortho-normal set of coordinate vectors $\mathbf{i}$, $\mathbf{j}$, $\mathbf{k}$, and 1 that we introduced in section 11, only here we will call them $\mathbf{c}_1$, $\mathbf{c}_2$, $\mathbf{c}_3$, and $\mathbf{c}_4$ (as we did at the end of section 24).   The orthonormality conditions are

29.1 $$\mathbf{c}_i \cdot \mathbf{c}_j = 0, \quad (\mathbf{c}_1)^2 = (\mathbf{c}_2)^2 = (\mathbf{c}_3)^2 = 1, \quad (\mathbf{c}_4)^2 = -1.$$

Let us review the equations of physics 12.1–12.5 from a formal point of view, especially as to the position of the indices.

Equation 12.1, $\partial_i(\rho u_i) = 0$, involves differentiation followed by contraction.   The differentiation index should be a subscript, as we know, and the two indices with respect to which contraction is performed should be on different levels.   We would expect, therefore, the equation to be written as

29.2 $$\partial_i(\rho u^i) = 0.$$

This does not mean that "$\mathbf{u}$ is a contravariant vector," but only that in this equation it should be represented by its contravariant components.   Incidentally, the equation defining u in the beginning of Chapter 3 should now be written

29.3 $$u^i = \frac{dx^i}{ds}.$$

Consider next one of the sets of Maxwell's equations, namely 12.2:

29.4 $$\partial_i F_{jk} + \partial_j F_{ki} + \partial_k F_{ij} = 0.$$

The index i appears in the first term as the result of differentiation and is thus properly a subscript.   It must therefore appear as a subscript also in the other terms, and the same applies to the other indices.   As far as this equation is concerned the tensor F must therefore be given by its *covariant* components.

Consider now equation 12.3,

$$\partial_j F_{ij} = \varepsilon u_i.$$

The reasoning we applied above to the continuity equation leads us to expect the index j of F to appear as a superscript.   The position of i is immaterial as far as this equation is concerned, but it must, of course, appear in the same position on both sides.   The equation must therefore be written

29.5 $\qquad\qquad \partial_j F^{ij} = \varepsilon u^i \qquad$ or $\qquad \partial_j F_i{}^j = \varepsilon u_i.$

We see thus that we should not use the same components of F in the two sets of Maxwell's equations.

In order to see what effect this has on the whole situation we remark that (compare exercise at the end of section 24) when we use coordinate vectors satisfying 29.1 the raising and lowering of indices has no effect on the components, except that the raising or lowering of the index 4 merely changes the sign of the component.   In other words, if we should want to rewrite equation $\partial_2 F_{34} + \partial_3 F_{42} + \partial_4 F_{23} = 0$, for example, using contravariant components, as in 29.5, we would have to write

$$-\partial_2 F^{34} - \partial_3 F^{42} + \partial_4 F^{23} = 0$$

or

$$\partial_2 F^{34} + \partial_3 F^{42} - \partial_4 F^{23} = 0.$$

We see that the minus sign appears exactly at the same place where it caused all the trouble in section 4.   We may say, then, that the trouble was due to the use of the wrong components.   More precisely, if we had made the same identification 4.5 there, but wrote the indices as superscripts so that

29.6
$$X = F^{41} \qquad Y = F^{42} \qquad Z = F^{43}$$
$$L = F^{23} \qquad M = F^{31} \qquad N = F^{12},$$

the first set of Maxwell's equations would have the nice form that it had with the indices in the proper places, and the other set would have the minus sign which disturbed the uniformity of notation only because we neglected to write the indices down where they belonged formally. Using the pseudo-orthonormal system we should then have written

Maxwell's equations as

$$\partial_i F_{jk} + \partial_j F_{ki} + \partial_k F_{ij} = 0,$$

$$\partial_j F^{ij} = \varepsilon u^i,$$

with the identifications 29.6, and we would have had no minus-sign trouble.

This seems to make the use of imaginary components unnecessary. Of course, the coordinate $t = x^4$ is also real now.

Proceeding with the equations of physics we find that 12.4 must be written

$$\partial_j T_i{}^j = 0 \qquad \text{or} \qquad \partial_j T^{ij} = 0,$$

and then, of course, we will have

29.61 $\qquad M^{ij} = \rho u^i u^j - g^{ij} p \qquad$ or $\qquad M_i{}^j = \rho u_i u^j - \delta_{ij} p.$

The electromagnetic stress-energy tensor also may be written in several forms, one of which is

29.62 $\qquad\qquad E_{ij} = F_i{}^k F_{kj} - \tfrac{1}{2} g_{ij} F_s{}^k F_k{}^s.$

Of course, as in 12.5 we have

29.63 $\qquad\qquad T_{ij} = M_{ij} - E_{ij}$

As the second step we consider a general coordinate system but still in a flat space. The ordinary derivatives of the components of a given tensor do not have any geometrical meaning here in that they are not the components of the differential of that tensor. The components of the differential are the covariant derivatives of the components of the given tensor. If we want the equations to have the same meaning in the general coordinates which they had in the ones we used before, we must write covariant derivatives for ordinary derivatives and the equations will appear as

29.71 $\qquad\qquad (\rho u^i)_{,i} = 0,$

29.72 $\qquad\qquad F_{ij,k} + F_{jk,i} + F_{ki,j} = 0,$

29.73 $\qquad\qquad F^{ij}{}_{,j} = \varepsilon u^i,$

29.74 $\qquad\qquad T^{ij}{}_{,j} = 0 \quad \text{or} \quad T_i{}^j{}_{,j} = 0.$

If we want to write these covariant derivatives explicitly we must use correction terms involving the Γ's, which in turn involve the g's. These g's can be calculated for the particular set of general coordinates we are using and we thus know how to rewrite our equations in general coordinates. But this is still just another way of writing the same equations. We have not changed their content. Using other than cartesian coordinates is sometimes a very convenient device; it is often practiced outside of the relativity theory, as for example when polar, elliptic coordinates or more general coordinates are used in elasticity theory. This does not, however, involve radical changes.

Now we introduce the third stage: curved space. The situation changes radically in that the content of the statements expressed by the equations, although they have the same form, is different if we interpret them in curved space. However, it is not enough to *say* that they refer to curved space. In order to have them have any meaning at all the g's must be given. Where do they come from? Here must be recalled how the idea of introducing curved space arose in the first place. We expected that the curvature of space-time would be connected with physical quantities—more precisely, that the complete tensor, and therefore all the quantities of classical physics that enter into it, would in some way be an expression of the structure of space. We found that the contracted corrected Riemann tensor satisfies the same equation that the complete tensor satisfies, namely $T^{ij}_{,j} = 0$. We therefore identify these two tensors and write

29.8 $$T_{ij} = R_{ij} - \tfrac{1}{2}g_{ij}R.$$

This gives meaning to the statement that equations 29.71–29.74 refer to curved space. *That curved space must be such that 29.8 holds.* The theory we have arrived at is expressed by equations 29.61, 29.62, 29.63, 29.71–29.74, and 29.8.

It is not enough, however, to have a theory. We must also know how to apply it. In other words, we must know how to identify the quantities appearing in the theory with quantities that we find as the result of measurements. There seems to be a difficulty here because we are accustomed to use ordinary flat space in the process of such identification. By introducing curved space in which there are no preferred coordinate systems we have lost some of the definiteness we are accustomed to. The coordinates should be considered now along with the other quantities ρ, u, v, w, p, X, Y, Z, L, M, N as the theoretical quantities that must be identified with measured quantities when the theory is applied. There is no question of what these quantities "really mean." The identification is correct if the theory is successful, that is, if it leads to correct predictions. Whether this is so we will see in the next chapter.

5

GENERAL RELATIVITY

In Chapter 1 certain fundamental quantities were introduced and combined into the symmetric tensor of rank two, T_{ij}. It was shown that this tensor satisfies the differential equation

$$\partial_j T_{ij} = 0,$$

for $i = 1, 2, 3$. In Chapter 3, as a result of the new identification introduced there, it was shown that it also held for $i = 4$. We attempted to build a mathematical theory in which a tensor of the same formal properties would appear in a natural way, and in Chapter 4 we succeeded in actually setting up such a theory—the theory of curved space-time.

The structure of such a space was found to be expressible in terms of a tensor of rank four, *the Riemann tensor*, from which a tensor of rank two, *the contracted Riemann tensor*, was obtained. In investigating the differential properties of the Riemann tensor we found in section 27 a relation of the type desired. It is, however, satisfied by a tensor which differs slightly from the contracted Riemann tensor, namely, the tensor $R^i_j - \frac{1}{2}\delta_{ij}R$, which we will call the *corrected contracted Riemann tensor*, and this is the tensor which we will identify with the physical tensor T so that our fundamental assumption will be

$$T^i_j = R^i_j - \frac{1}{2}\delta_{ij}R.$$

Thus we decide to interpret T and, therefore, our fundamental quantities of matter and electricity ρ, u, v, w, p, X, Y, Z, L, M, N, which went into it, in terms of structure of curved space as it is reflected in the contracted corrected Riemann tensor. But in doing this we face a radically different situation. As was desired, the tensor is now an expression of the properties of space, but the space is now different from the one we had before in that geometry and physics are now an organic whole. We want to investigate the implications of this change. Along with the desirable feature that T grew out of space, so to say, we may have brought in some not too desirable and hard-to-manage features. But then, there would be no advantage if we could merely *say* that T is a geometrical thing now. We expected to gain something essential by merging geometry and physics together. This has now been accomplished, and we have to see what it brought with it. We constructed something the implications of which we are unable to stop, and we have to go ahead and hope that they will be beneficial.

It might seem strange that a physical interpretation exists for the contracted Riemann tensor alone, since it involves only ten combinations of its twenty components. But this is quite in order. If all the components of the Riemann tensor were used up in interpreting matter and electricity it would mean that in the absence of matter (and electricity) space-time would be flat as far as internal properties were concerned. This, in turn, would mean that matter acted only where it was. However, we know that matter makes itself felt (for instance, by the gravitational field that it produces) outside the region it occupies. This is in accord with our identification as a result of which only part of the components of the Riemann tensor vanish where there is no matter, so that the remaining components may be interpreted as corresponding to gravitational effects.

30. The law of geodesics

In the questions of celestial mechanics which we are now going to treat, the effects of the electromagnetic field and pressure are usually negligible, and so we shall begin by equating both of them to zero. Equation 29.63 then becomes

30.1 $$T_j^i = \rho u^i u_j.$$

According to the fundamental assumption, this tensor must be identical with the corrected contracted Riemann tensor, and it must therefore satisfy the equation

30.2 $$T^j_{i,j} = 0,$$

which *formally* is the same as our old equation of motion 12.4, but which differs from it in that it has to be interpreted in curved space. The last two equations, 30.1 and 30.2, impose certain conditions on the velocity components u^i, and we want to determine these conditions, or, in other words, we want to eliminate density from equations 30.1 and 30.2.

First of all we shall prove the following theorem:

THEOREM.   If equations 30.1 and 30.2 are satisfied, the vectors u^i may be considered tangent vectors to a family of geodesics which fill the space.

Proof.   To demonstrate this we must show, according to section 28, that it is possible to choose the parameters on the curves in such a way that the tangent vectors to the curves obtained by differentiation with respect to these parameters satisfy equation 28.2.   The vectors u^i in formula 30.1 are tangent vectors obtained by differentiation with respect to certain parameters.   This was the definition of the u^i which is at the basis of the identification introduced in the beginning of Chapter 4.   If the vectors u^i satisfy 28.2, the theorem is proved. If they do not, the curves that have the u^i as tangent vectors still may be geodesics because it may be that 28.2 will be satisfied for a different choice of parameters.   The change of parameters is equivalent to multiplication of the tangent vectors by a function λ.   To show that the curves are geodesics it is sufficient then to prove the existence of a function λ such that the vectors $v^i = \lambda u^i$ satisfy the relation 28.2, which can be written

$$(\partial_j \lambda) \cdot u^i \cdot \lambda u^j + \lambda u^i{}_{,j} \cdot \lambda u^j = 0.$$

Now if we denote $\log \lambda$ by μ, this becomes

30.3 $$(\partial_j \mu) u^i u^j + u^i{}_{,j} u^j = 0.$$

On the other hand, from 30.1 and 30.2 it follows (if $\log \rho$ is denoted by σ) that

30.4 $$(\partial_j \sigma) \cdot u^i u^j + u^i{}_{,j} u^j + u^i u^j{}_{,j} = 0.$$

Subtracting this from 30.3, we obtain

$$\partial_j (\mu - \sigma) \cdot u^i u^j - u^i u^j{}_{,j} = 0.$$

This will be satisfied if

30.5 $$\frac{\partial (\mu - \sigma)}{\partial x^j} \cdot u^j = u^j{}_{,j}.$$

This is an equation in partial derivatives for a function $\mu - \sigma$.   Denoting a solution of this equation by ψ we have

$$\mu - \sigma = \psi.$$

and from this

$$\lambda = e^\mu = e^\sigma \cdot e^\psi = \rho e^\psi.$$

The theorem is therefore proved.

We conclude that in a gravitational field matter and light particles follow geodesics.

In the present chapter we are going to apply this result to the investigation of the motion of a planet and the propagation of light in the solar system. We shall see that the changed significance of differentiation takes care, in a way, of the effects usually accounted for by gravitational forces.

31. Solar system.   Symmetry conditions

Equations 30.1 and 30.2 describe relations existing between matter and field. On the one hand, we have proved that the motion of matter is characterized by the geodesics of the curved space. On the other hand, equation 30.1 shows that the curvature is in turn determined by matter. Theoretically, we have a complete description of the situation, but in practice we do not know how to handle it, since we do not know where to begin. It may seem that we are in the midst of a vicious circle, but situations like this occur often in mathematics. One way to handle them is to resort to the method of successive approximations. Let us try to apply this method here. In investigating the motion of a planet around the sun we neglect in the first place the motion of the sun. Then, in the first approximation we neglect the mass of the planet, i.e., we assume that there is no matter outside the sun. Since we have already neglected electromagnetism it then follows that outside the sun the tensor T is zero so that, according to the fundamental assumption,

$$R^i_j - \tfrac{1}{2}\delta_{ij}R = 0.$$

Contraction gives $R - \tfrac{1}{2} \cdot 4R = 0$, so $R = 0$, and we have simply

31.1 $R^i_j = 0.$

These equations are known as Einstein's equations. The statement that the *corrected* contracted Riemann tensor vanishes is thus seen to be equivalent to the statement that the contracted Riemann tensor vanishes.

As a result of our first approximation we derived the field equations 31.1. In the next approximation we introduce the planet and assume that its action on the field is negligible but that the field acts on it, i.e., that the motion of the planet is given by the geodesics of the field which has been determined in the preceding step. The motions will then be given by the equations (compare 28.1; dots indicate differentiation with respect to a parameter which in the case of matter is arc length)

31.2 $$\ddot{x}^i + \Gamma^i_{ks}\dot{x}^k\dot{x}^s = 0,$$

in which the Γ's are calculated from the g's which were determined by the condition that equation 31.1 are satisfied.

Our problem, therefore, decomposes into two: first, to find a field satisfying equations 31.1; and second, to find the geodesics of this field.

In this form the problem is comparable to the problem in Newtonian mechanics explained in section 1. There the field was given by the potential which had to satisfy the Laplace equation. Here the field is given by the g's which have to satisfy equations 31.1. There the motion, after the field had been determined, was described by second-order ordinary differential equations, differentiation being taken with respect to time. Here motion is also described by second-order differential equations, differentiation in the case of matter being with respect to s.

It is possible by making some special assumptions (for example, neglecting certain quantities, as the derivatives of all the g's except g_{44}, and dropping some terms) to obtain the general Newtonian equations as a special or limiting case of our equations. Equations 31.1 would thus reduce to the Laplace equation 1.54 for g_{44}, and the equations of a geodesic to the equations of motion 1.1 in which X, Y, Z are given by 1.53. Thus general Newtonian Theory of motion in a gravitational field could be considered a first approximation to the theory of relativity, but it is quite difficult in the general case to estimate what is neglected and the error that is committed, and we prefer, therefore, to compare the two theories in some concrete special cases. All of them will correspond to a gravitational field produced by a single attracting center.

In section 1 such a field was found by using the general equations and, in addition, the condition of symmetry. We intend to follow an analogous course here. Our general equations are now 31.1, and we want to find what will correspond to the conditions of symmetry. The situation is much more complicated here than it was in section 1, where we had a vector field, for we now have a quadratic differential form. In the second place, in section 1 we worked in ordinary space whereas we now have space-time and hence the additional coordinate, t. Finally, in section 1 the space was *given;* in it distances were well defined; and a field whose symmetry we had to discuss was superimposed on it. Here the field is not superimposed on a space with a given metric, but the metric itself constitutes a field that has to be determined by the symmetry condition.

We shall take up these three difficulties one by one.

In the first place consider a quadratic form $g_{ij} \, dx^i \, dx^j$ (with i and j taking the values from 1 to 3) in flat, three-dimensional space. A quadratic form may be considered (section 10) as the left-hand side of the equation of an ellipsoid. We have then at every point P of space instead of a vector, with P as initial point, as in section 1, an ellipsoid with P as center. As there, the field must permit rotations around a fixed center O; i.e., such a rotation must bring the field into itself. In other words, if a rotation brings a point P into a point Q it must bring the ellipsoid at P into the ellipsoid at Q. In particular, a rotation that leaves P unchanged must not change the ellipsoid at P. It is clear that every ellipsoid must be an ellipsoid of revolution and that its axis must be directed along the radius vector from O to P.

Now introduce spherical coordinates (compare exercise, section 23, p. 116). The vector c_1 will have the direction OP, and so it will lie on the axis of revolution of the ellipsoid, and c_2 and c_3 will be perpendicular to it. If the directions of these vectors are used as coordinate axes and P is used as the origin a vector with initial point P may be written $\xi c_1 + \eta c_2 + \zeta c_3$. And if the end point of this vector is on the surface of the ellipsoid the coordinates of that point will be $\xi c_1, \eta c_2, \zeta c_3$; these coordinates must satisfy an equation of the type

$$A(\xi c_1)^2 + B(\eta c_2)^2 + B(\zeta c_3)^2 = 1.$$

The last two coefficients are equal, because the ellipsoid has two equal axes. Using the results of the exercise mentioned above, the left-hand side of this equation can be written

$$A\xi^2 + Br^2(\eta^2 + \sin^2\theta \, \zeta^2).$$

Since every two ellipsoids whose centers are at the same distance from O can be brought into coincidence by a rotation the coefficients A and B must be functions of r alone. Denoting $r^2 B$ by B' and introducing the customary differential notation for the increments ξ, η, ζ of the coordinates r, θ, and ϕ we finally arrive at the expression

$$A \, dr^2 + B'(d\theta^2 + \sin^2\theta \, d\phi^2)$$

for a field of quadratic forms which satisfies the requirement of symmetry with respect to a point.

Next, consider the complication resulting from the introduction of time. In section 1, time was not mentioned, and so the field was considered independent of time, or static. We may say that the field must not be affected by a change in t, or, from the four-dimensional

point of view, by a translation along the t axis.   This is a requirement
of the same character as that of symmetry with respect to a point.
From the four-dimensional point of view the two requirements may
be combined so that we may say that the field must be symmetric
with respect to a line, the t axis.   But as the field is now a field in
four-space, it will be represented by a quadratic form in dr, $d\theta$, $d\phi$,
and dt.   For $dt = 0$ it must reduce to the field given before.   Thus
the coefficients must be independent of t, corresponding to the requirement that the field is static: under these conditions a change from t
to $-t$ must also not affect the field (reversibility of time), and so terms
of the quadratic form involving dt to the first power must be absent.
It follows then that the addition of the fourth dimension results in the
addition of only one term to the tensor, which now may be written

31.4 $$A\,dr^2 + B'(d\theta^2 + \sin^2\theta\,d\phi^2) + C\,dt^2,$$

where C, as well as A and B', are functions of r alone.

Now we have to overcome the last difficulty, which is connected
with the fact that our space is curved and that we cannot define symmetry in terms of rotations because rotation implies a transformation
in which distances are preserved.   But here distances are defined
by the field of the g's which we want to determine by the requirement
that it be not affected by rotations.   To overcome this difficulty it is
necessary to use some other definition for symmetry, and it seems
natural to adopt the following idea.   In order to define a symmetry
for a curved space we shall compare it with a flat space by establish-
ing a one-to-one correspondence between the points of the two spaces.
Corresponding to every transformation of the flat space we will have
then a transformation of the curved space.   We shall say that the
curved space possesses the same symmetry as a field F in the flat
space if the metric of the curved space, as given by the g's, is not
affected by those transformations of the curved space that correspond
to the transformations in flat space that do not affect the field F.

Suppose now that we have such a curved space.   This implies that
we have a one-to-one correspondence with the flat space, and we may
use the same coordinates for the points of curved space as for the corresponding points of the flat space.   It is clear that 31.4 satisfies the
symmetry requirements, and so we can take it for our fundamental
tensor, or as we shall say (compare 24.51) for our ds^2.

However, the quantities r, θ, ϕ, t, which have definite geometrical
significance in flat space, lose it in curved space; they are just numbers
used to characterize different points as numbers are used to charac-

terize houses on a street. There is no reason why they should not be replaced by other numbers, i.e., why the coordinates should not be transformed, if it would simplify the formulas. Now, it is clear that transformations involving θ, ϕ, t will make expression 31.4 more complicated because they would introduce these coordinates into the coefficients. But we could choose a transformation on r alone which would simplify that expression; for example, reduce any one coefficient to a prescribed function of the new r. Let us make this choice in such a way as to reduce B' to r^2 because, in a way, it restores to r a geometrical meaning, as we shall see presently. If we write $\xi(r)$ and $-\eta(r)$ for the functions of the new r which now appear instead of A and C, and interpret 31.4 as giving $-ds^2$, in accordance with the standardization of the parameter adopted in section 13, our final formula will be

31.5 $-ds^2 = \xi(r)\, dr^2 + r^2(d\theta^2 + \sin^2\theta\, d\phi^2) - \eta(r)\, dt^2.$

When r and t have constant values we have a surface, and a simple calculation would show that $1/r^2$ is the total curvature of this surface. This gives a geometrical meaning to r. We can say that r is the radius of a sphere which has the same curvature as the surface $t =$ constant, $r =$ constant, in the curved space we are considering.

Our task is now accomplished, in that we have imposed the conditions of symmetry on our space. Next we have to impose on it the general equations 31.1.

32. Solution of the field equations

We are now at a stage which corresponds to the assumption of section 1, that the potential ϕ is a function of r alone, and our next task corresponds to the substitution of $\phi(r)$ into Laplace's equation. Here, instead of one unknown function $\phi(r)$, we have the g's determined by 31.5, which we write out as

32.1 $g_{11} = \xi(r), \qquad g_{22} = r^2, \qquad g_{33} = r^2 \sin^2\theta, \qquad g_{44} = -\eta(r),$

all others zero,

and which involve two unknown functions. In order to determine these functions we have to substitute 32.1 into 31.1. In the first place we have to calculate the g's with the upper indices from the formulas (compare exercise 2, section 24)

$$g_{ik}g^{kj} = \delta_{ij}.$$

Since the g's with two distinct lower indices vanish, only those terms on the left in which $k = i$ are not zero, and we have

$$g_{ii}g^{ij} = \delta_{ij}.$$

For $i \neq j$ the right-hand sides are zero, and since the first factors on the left are not zero the second must vanish.   We see thus that the g's with two distinct upper indices also vanish.   For $j = i$ we have unity on the right, and thus

32.2 $g^{11} = \dfrac{1}{\xi(r)},$ $g^{22} = \dfrac{1}{r^2},$ $g^{33} = \dfrac{1}{r^2 \sin^2 \theta},$ $g^{44} = -\dfrac{1}{\eta(r)};$

all others zero.

In the following, let

$$x^1 = r, \qquad x^2 = \theta, \qquad x^3 = \phi, \qquad x^4 = t,$$

and denote differentiation with respect to r, as in section 1, by prime. Next we calculate the Γ's with all indices down according to 25.52, and obtain, omitting those that are zero,

32.3

$$\Gamma_{1,11} = \tfrac{1}{2}\xi', \qquad \Gamma_{1,22} = -r, \qquad \Gamma_{1,33} = -r \sin^2 \theta, \qquad \Gamma_{1,44} = \tfrac{1}{2}\eta',$$

$$\Gamma_{2,33} = -r^2 \sin \theta \cos \theta, \qquad \Gamma_{2,12} = r,$$

$$\Gamma_{3,13} = r \sin^2 \theta, \qquad \Gamma_{3,23} = r^2 \sin \theta \cos \theta$$

$$\Gamma_{4,14} = -\tfrac{1}{2}\eta'.$$

To raise an index here it is merely necessary to multiply by the g with that index repeated as a superscript, because the sum $g^{ik}F_k$ which, according to 24.4, is equal to F^i reduces to one term, $g^{ii}F_i$, since all the g's with two unequal upper indices vanish.   This permits us to write out easily the Γ's with one index above:

32.31

$$\Gamma_{11}^1 = \dfrac{\xi'}{2\xi}, \qquad \Gamma_{22}^1 = -\dfrac{r}{\xi}, \qquad \Gamma_{33}^1 = -\dfrac{r \sin^2 \theta}{\xi}, \qquad \Gamma_{44}^1 = \dfrac{\eta'}{2\xi},$$

$$\Gamma_{33}^2 = -\sin \theta \cos \theta, \qquad \Gamma_{12}^2 = \dfrac{1}{r},$$

$$\Gamma_{13}^3 = \dfrac{1}{r}, \qquad \Gamma_{23}^3 = \cot \theta, \qquad \Gamma_{14}^4 = \dfrac{\eta'}{2\eta}.$$

Next we have to calculate those components of the Riemann tensor that appear in the expressions for the components of the contracted Riemann tensor, i.e., those with the first index equal to the one before last, or those of the type $R^i_{j;ik}$.   We will not write these out but will

merely state that the result of the calculation of the components of
the contracted Riemann tensor with their aid is that all components
with two distinct indices vanish while the others are

$$R_{11} = \frac{\xi'}{\xi r} + \frac{\xi' \eta'}{4\xi\eta} + \frac{\eta'^2}{4\eta^2} - \frac{\eta''}{2\eta},$$

$$R_{22} = \frac{\xi' r}{2\xi^2} + \left(1 - \frac{1}{\xi}\right) - \frac{r\eta'}{2\xi\eta},$$

$$R_{33} = R_{22} \sin \theta,$$

$$R_{44} = - \frac{\xi' \eta'}{4\xi^2} - \frac{\eta'^2}{4\xi\eta} + \frac{\eta''}{2\xi} + \frac{\eta'}{\xi r}.$$

It is more convenient to operate with the mixed components of the
contracted Riemann tensor (although it is not necessary, and the reader
might for the sake of practice go through the same calculations using
covariant components). These are obtained from the above formulas
upon multiplication by the corresponding g with upper indices. The
result of this operation gives

$$R_1^1 = \frac{\xi'}{\xi^2 r} + \frac{\xi' \eta'}{4\xi^2 \eta} + \frac{\eta'^2}{4\xi\eta^2} - \frac{\eta''}{2\xi\eta}$$

32.4
$$\left. \begin{array}{l} R_2^2 = \\ R_3^3 = \end{array} \right\} \frac{\xi'}{2\xi^2 r} + \frac{1}{r^2}\left(1 - \frac{1}{\xi}\right) - \frac{\eta'}{2\xi\eta r},$$

$$R_4^4 = \frac{\xi' \eta'}{4\xi^2 \eta} + \frac{\eta'^2}{4\eta^2 \xi} - \frac{\eta''}{2\xi\eta} - \frac{\eta'}{\xi\eta r}.$$

We come now to the ten equations $R_j^i = 0$ that must be satisfied. Six
of them, namely, those in which $i \neq j$, are satisfied identically because
the R's are well as the δ's vanish for distinct indices. Of the remaining
four equations the second and the third are identically the same
because of the equality of the corresponding expressions for R in 32.4.
Three equations remain, viz.,

$$\frac{\xi'}{\xi^2 r} + \frac{\xi' \eta'}{4\xi^2 \eta} + \frac{\eta'^2}{4\xi\eta^2} - \frac{\eta''}{2\xi\eta} = 0,$$

32.5
$$\frac{\xi'}{2\xi^2 r} + \frac{1}{r^2}\left(1 - \frac{1}{\xi}\right) - \frac{\eta'}{2\xi\eta r} = 0,$$

$$\frac{\xi' \eta'}{4\xi^2 \eta} + \frac{\eta'^2}{4\eta^2 \xi} - \frac{\eta''}{2\xi\eta} - \frac{\eta'}{\xi\eta r} = 0.$$

Subtracting the last one from the first gives

32.6 $$\frac{1}{\xi r}\left(\frac{\xi'}{\xi} + \frac{\eta'}{\eta}\right) = 0,$$

whence

$$\xi\eta = \text{constant}$$

By choosing the unit of time appropriately this constant can be reduced to 1, so that

32.7 $$\xi\eta = 1 \qquad \text{or} \qquad \xi = \frac{1}{\eta}.$$

Using 32.6 and 32.7 in the second of the equations 32.5 gives

$$\eta' r = 1 - \eta,$$

so that

32.8 $$\eta = 1 - \frac{\gamma}{r},$$

where γ denotes a constant of integration.

The field then is given by

32.9 $$-ds^2 = \frac{dr^2}{\eta} + r^2\, d\theta^2 + r^2 \sin^2\theta\, d\phi^2 - \eta\, dt^2,$$

where η is given by 32.8.

33. Equations of geodesics

Consider first the non-zero geodesics which correspond to a material particle. We know that in this case arc length can be taken as parameter so that the curve must satisfy the equation 31.5 in addition to the equations 31.2. These may be written as

33.1 $$\frac{\dot{r}^2}{\eta} + r^2\dot{\theta}^2 + r^2 \sin^2\theta\dot{\phi}^2 - \eta\dot{t}^2 = -1;$$

We shall, however, make our discussion slightly more general and write A for the right-hand side so that the results can also be used in the case corresponding to a light particle. We shall discuss this equation together with equations 31.2, which, using the expressions 32.31 for the Γ's, may be written

33.21 $$\ddot{r} - \frac{\eta'}{2\eta}\cdot\dot{r}^2 + r\eta\cdot\dot{\theta}^2 + r\eta \sin^2\theta\cdot\dot{\phi}^2 + \frac{\eta\eta'}{2}\cdot\dot{t}^2 = 0$$

33.22 $$\ddot{\theta} + \frac{\dot{r}}{2r} \cdot \dot{\theta} - \sin\theta \cos\theta\, \dot{\phi}^2 = 0,$$

33.23 $$\ddot{\phi} + 2\frac{\dot{r}}{r} \cdot \dot{\phi} + 2\cot\theta \cdot \dot{\theta}\dot{\phi} = 0,$$

33.24 $$\ddot{t} + \frac{\eta'}{\eta} \cdot \dot{r}\dot{t} = 0.$$

The choice of the θ and ϕ coordinates is at our disposal. We choose them in such a way that the initial position of the particle is on the equator and that the tangent is tangent to the equator. In this case $\theta = \pi/2$ and $\dot{\theta} =$ zero at the initial moment, and the second equation shows that $\theta = \pi/2$ always. Now the last two equations may be integrated once each and they furnish

33.3 $$\dot{\phi}r^2 = h$$

33.4 $$\dot{t}\eta = k$$

where h and k are constants. Together with these two equations we have to consider the one corresponding to 33.1; viz.,

33.5 $$\frac{\dot{r}^2}{\eta} + r^2\dot{\phi}^2 - \eta\dot{t}^2 = A.$$

We simplify the system of equations in the following way: (a) we eliminate t by means of 33.4; (b) we eliminate differentiation with respect to the parameter by using $\dot{r} = (dr/d\phi) \cdot \dot{\phi}$ and 33.3; (c) we introduce as a new variable, as is customary in celestial mechanics, the inverse distance $u = 1/r$, instead of r, so that

33.6 $$r = \frac{1}{u};$$

and, (d) we substitute the value for η from 32.8. We obtain in this way a differential equation between u and ϕ, viz.,

33.7 $$\left(\frac{du}{d\phi}\right)^2 + u^2 = \lambda - A\frac{\gamma}{h^2}u + \gamma u^3,$$

where γ is a constant. This may be considered the equation for the orbit of a planet.

34. Newtonian motion of a planet

Every reader knows, of course, that according to the Newtonian theory a planet moves around the sun on an ellipse at one of whose foci the sun is situated, although he may not be in possession of a proof. We shall not give a proof here either, but we shall discuss in detail one feature of the situation. The vertex of the ellipse that is · nearest to the focus in which the sun is located is called the perihelion; the other vertex, the aphelion. The line joining the perihelion and the aphelion is the major axis and therefore passes through the sun. Using the coordinates u and ϕ corresponding to those of the preceding section we may say that the perihelion corresponds to the maximum value of u, and the aphelion to the minimum value of u, and that the transition from the maximum to the minimum value of u corresponds to the change of ϕ by the amount π. It is this last fact that we shall deduce from the equations of motion. We may (corresponding to the fact that we set $\theta = \frac{1}{2}\pi$ in the preceding section) consider a motion in the x-y plane characterized by the equations (see 1.1 and 1.3, and introduction to Chapter 4)

34.1
$$\frac{d^2x}{dt^2} + \frac{Mx}{r^3} = 0, \qquad \frac{d^2y}{dt^2} + \frac{My}{r^3} = 0.$$

Now form the expressions

34.2 $\qquad H = xy' - yx' \qquad$ and $\qquad K = x'^2 + y'^2 - \dfrac{2M}{r},$

where primes indicate differentiation with respect to time. Differentiating H and K and taking into account 34.1 we find that the derivatives are zero, and so these quantities are constant (that is, remain constant during the motion). Equations 34.2 are, as one says, first integrals of the system 34.1; the integral of areas and the integral of energy respectively. To facilitate comparison with relativity treatment, introduce the variables ϕ and u by the formulas

34.3 $\qquad\qquad x = \dfrac{\cos \phi}{u}, \qquad y = \dfrac{\sin \phi}{u},$

so that equations 34.2 become

34.4 $\qquad\qquad H = \dfrac{\phi'}{u^2}, \qquad K = \dfrac{\phi'^2}{u^2} + \dfrac{u'^2}{u^4} - 2Mu.$

We are interested in the orbit rather than in the motion on that orbit: in other words, not in the dependence of ϕ and u on time but in their dependence on each other, or again not in ϕ' and u' but in $du/d\phi$, which is equal to u'/ϕ'. From 34.4 we have

$$\frac{\phi'^2}{u^4} = H^2, \qquad \frac{\phi'^2}{u^2} + \frac{u'^2}{u^4} = K + 2Mu.$$

Dividing the second of these equations by the first we get

34.5 $$\left(\frac{du}{d\phi}\right)^2 + u^2 = \frac{K}{H^2} + \frac{2M}{H^2}\, u.$$

This corresponds to equation 33.7 obtained from relativity theory in the preceding section. In that last equation we have, of course, to take $A = -1$ when we consider the motion of a planet so that it becomes

34.51 $$\left(\frac{du}{d\phi}\right)^2 + u^2 = \lambda + \frac{\gamma u}{h^2} + \gamma u^3,$$

and we see therefore that the difference is, essentially, due to only one term. But before we come to the comparison of the motions described by these two equations we have to continue the discussion of 34.5. The character of motion described by it depends on the values of the constants appearing in it, and also on the initial conditions. We begin the discussion by writing 34.5 in the form

34.52 $$\left(\frac{du}{d\phi}\right)^2 = -(u - u_1)(u - u_2),$$

where u_1 and u_2 are the two roots of the quadratic polynomial $u^2 - 2Mu/H^2 - K/H^2$. If the two roots are complex, or equal, the right-hand side of 34.52 is negative and we cannot have real motion. Also when both roots are negative the right-hand side is negative for positive values of u (and u, being the inverse distance, must be positive). The case of one positive and one negative root corresponds to u changing from zero to a finite value and then going back to zero: for example, a comet approaching the sun from an infinite distance and then receding back into infinity. But we want to discuss the motion of a planet, and this will obviously correspond to the only remaining case, viz., that of two distinct positive roots. If by u_1 we denote the larger and by u_2 the smaller of the two roots it will be convenient to write our equation as

34.53 $$\left(\frac{du}{d\phi}\right)^2 = (u_1 - u)(u - u_2),$$

and we see that a real solution is possible only when u is between u_2 and u_1. The motion will manifest itself in an oscillation of u between

u_2 and u_1, and the sign of $du/d\phi$ will change at these points. The particular question we want to investigate is, as was mentioned at the beginning of the section, the change of ϕ corresponding to one oscillation of u, say between u_2 and u_1. In order to determine this we solve the equation for $d\phi$, obtaining

$$d\phi = \frac{du}{\sqrt{(u_1 - u)(u - u_2)}},$$

whence

34.6 $$\phi_1 - \phi_2 = \int_{u_2}^{u_1} \frac{du}{\sqrt{(u_1 - u)(u - u_2)}}.$$

A change of variable will help us to evaluate this integral. Set

34.7 $$\frac{u - u_2}{u_1 - u_2} = \sin^2 x$$

so that, when x changes from 0 to $\pi/2$, u will increase from u_2 to u_1 as required. We have

$$du = 2(u_1 - u_2) \sin x \cos x \, dx,$$

34.8 $\quad u - u_2 = (u_1 - u_2) \sin^2 x,$

$$u_1 - u = u_1 - [u_2 + (u_1 - u_2) \sin^2 x] = (u_1 - u_2) \cos^2 x.$$

The integral becomes

34.9 $$\phi_1 - \phi_2 = \int_0^{\pi/2} 2dx = \pi.$$

The answer to our question is, then, that ϕ changes exactly by π as u performs an oscillation between its minimum and its maximum values. This corresponds to the fact mentioned above that the aphelion and the perihelion are on a straight line with the sun, a fact we have now established.

35. Relativity motion of a planet

Following this excursion into Newtonian celestial mechanics we return to our relativity formulas, which we shall compare to the formulas derived in the last section.

At this stage we come again upon a fundamental point. We have two theories. The quantities of one of them have been identified with measured quantities, and identification proved, in the main, a splendid success. If the new theory is to be applied successfully, it is clear that it must essentially agree with the old theory with which it may be compared instead of being compared with results of measurement directly. This means that we have to establish a correspondence between quantities of the two theories, and we must be able to show that the corresponding quantities of the two theories obey approximately the same relations. This correspondence has been anticipated in the preceding pages in that the same letters have been used for quantities which will be identified. But it may not be superfluous to remind the reader that the quantities u, ϕ, θ of the two theories are not the same. There is a certain arbitrariness in the choice of coordinates in curved space. This is especially obvious in the case of r (of which u is the inverse), for it is possible to substitute some simple function of r for r. The only criterion is the success of the identification.

Next we must identify the constants of the new theory with those of the old. It would seem as though we must, in order to reach an agreement, make $\gamma = 0$ so as to eliminate the last term of the equation 34.51 by which it differs essentially from 34.5. But this would annihilate the preceding term in the new formula also and so spoil the correspondence altogether. We must, therefore, ascribe to γ a finite value, which we will expect to be small. More precisely, it will be small in such a way that the term γu^3 will not affect the equation 34.51 essentially, or, in other words, it will be small in comparison with u^2. Next, let us compare 33.3 with 34.4. Of course, the left-hand sides differ by the factor dt/ds, but this is equal (compare section 14) to $1/\sqrt{1 - \beta^2}$, which is, even for the motions of the planets, very close to 1, so that, in the first approximation, we may identify h with H. Comparison of 34.5 with 34.51 shows that

35.1 $\gamma = 2M,$

so that we may write 34.51 as

35.2 $$\left(\frac{du}{d\phi}\right)^2 + u^2 = \lambda + \frac{2Mu}{H^2} + 2Mu^3.$$

After we have made these identifications the situation is then this: if we neglect the term $2Mu^3$ in the equation, and this term is negligible in most cases, we have the same equation of the orbit as in Newtonian mechanics. This result is very satisfactory in that we have been able to obtain the equations of the orbit of a planet without the consideration of any gravitational forces, as a result of our identification of the contracted Riemann tensor with the complete tensor. Still the term $2Mu^3$ is there, so that the relativity theory predicts an orbit that is slightly different from that predicted by the Newtonian theory.

Is the difference within the error of observation? Instead of considering the motion as a whole, we shall consider only the feature of it which was discussed in the preceding section for Newtonian motion; viz., we shall ask ourselves whether, corresponding to an oscillation of u between a minimum and a maximum value, the change in ϕ will be exactly π. Of course, we are sure that in the new theory there will be motions which differ but slightly from the motion considered in the preceding section, so that the general character of the motion will be the same, and u will oscillate between a minimum and maximum. The square of $du/d\phi$ will now be expressed by a polynomial of degree *three*, the first two terms of which are

$$2Mu^3 - u^2.$$

The sum of the three roots of this polynomial is $1/2M$ so that if u_1, u_2 denote two roots, viz., those two roots that differ but slightly from the roots denoted in the same way in section 34, the third root will be

$$\frac{1}{2M} - u_1 - u_2,$$

and the integral corresponding to 34.6 will be

$$\int_{u_2}^{u_1} \frac{du}{\sqrt{(u_1 - u)(u - u_2)[1 - (u_1 + u_2 + u)2M]}}.$$

The same substitution 34.7 as before will be applied. We only have to calculate

$$u_1 + u_2 + u = u_1 + u_2 + u_2 + (u_1 - u_2) \sin^2 x$$

$$= u_1 + u_2 + u_1 \sin^2 x + u_2 \cos^2 x.$$

so that the integral becomes

$$\phi_1 - \phi_2 = \int_0^{\pi/2} \frac{2dx}{\sqrt{1 - 2M(u_1 + u_2 + u_1 \sin^2 x + u_2 \cos^2 x)}}.$$

As we saw before, M is a very small quantity. Previously, we neglected it altogether and obtained π for the value of the integral. Now, we shall go to the next approximation. We shall develop the denominator according to powers of M and neglect all terms beyond the second (it would be a very easy but not a worthwhile matter to estimate the value of the error). We obtain in this way, as an approximate value for $\phi_1 - \phi_2$,

$$\int_0^{\pi/2} 2[1 + M(u_1 + u_2 + u_1 \sin^2 x + u_2 \cos^2 x)] \, dx.$$

This is, however,

$$\pi + \frac{3\pi M}{2} (u_1 + u_2).$$

The new theory predicts then that the angle ϕ will have changed by this amount while the distance from the sun changes from its minimum to its maximum; i.e., that the perihelion and aphelion are not in a straight line with the sun but that the planet moves through an additional angle of $3\pi M/2 \cdot (u_1 + u_2)$ after reaching the position opposite the one where it was during the perihelion, before reaching the aphelion. Since the same situation applies to the motion between an aphelion and the next perihelion we see that between two consecutive perihelia the planet will have moved through $2\pi + 3\pi M(u_1 + u_2)$, or that the perhelion will have moved through an angle $3\pi M(u_1 + u_2)$ during one full revolution of the planet. This is a very small amount, and it may be considered a correction to the classical result according to which the planet moves on an elliptic orbit with the sun at one of the foci. If a is the major semi-axis and e the eccentricity, the distance at perihelion is $a - ae$ and the distance at aphelion is $a + ae$; we have then

$$u_1 + u_2 = \frac{1}{(a - ae)} + \frac{1}{(a + ae)} = \frac{2}{a(1 - e^2)},$$

and the final formula for the advance of the perihelion is

35.5
$$p = \frac{6\pi M}{a(1 - e^2)}.$$

Here then we have two predictions: in the old theory the perihelion will remain fixed in space; according to the new one it will advance by p during one revolution. What are the observed results? For most planets either this amount is too small or the position of the perihelion too uncertain to permit any decision but in respect to the planet Mercury it had been known for a long time that there was a discrepancy between the prediction of the Newtonian theory and actual observations. It happens that the discrepancy is very nearly the amount showing the discrepancy between the two theories, so that the theory of relativity predicts a result that has actually been observed. This must be considered a success for the new theory.

36. Deflection of light

According to section 30 a light particle also moves along a geodesic, only for a light particle it is a zero geodesic along which the tangent vectors have zero length.   The equations for such a geodesic are the same as for the other kind with the difference that the parameter is no longer arc length.   As a result we have to replace -1 in the right-hand member of equation 33.1 by zero, that is, make $A = 0$ in equations 33.5 and 33.7.   The equation of the orbit therefore (taking into account 35.1) will be.

36.1 $$\left(\frac{du}{d\phi}\right)^2 + u^2 = \lambda + 2Mu^3.$$

This will have to be compared with the same equation without the term containing u^3, which is an equation of a straight line and characterizes the propagation of a beam of light in the old theory.   In fact, the equation of a straight line whose distance from the origin is $1/p$ and which is perpendicular to the polar axis is, in our coordinates, $u = p \cos \phi$.   We have then that $du/d\phi = -p \sin \phi$, so that, taking the sum of the squares of the last two expressions, we find that they add up to p^2, which we may identify with λ.   Again the term $2Mu^3$ is very small because the maximum value u can take is the inverse of the minimum value of the distance from the center of the sun, which is the radius of the sun.   We treat the problem again as a perturbation problem.   That is, we compare the required solution to that of the equation without the $2Mu^3$ term.   Again we are interested in the change of the angle ϕ corresponding to a transition between the two extreme values of u.   We shall be interested in a beam of light emitted from a star, which, before arriving at our telescope, passes very near to the surface of the sun.   The distances of the star and even of the earth from the sun are very large in comparison with the minimum distance, and we shall take them as infinite.   The maximum value of u, corresponding to the minimum distance from the sun, we shall denote by u_0.   Since $du/d\phi$ changes its sign when the light particle reaches this point it must vanish there.   The left-hand side of 36.1 reduces to u_0^2, so that

$$u_0^2 = \lambda + 2Mu_0^3.$$

Using the value for λ obtained from this relation, equation 36.1 becomes

$$\left(\frac{du}{d\phi}\right)^2 + u^2 = u_0^2 - 2Mu_0^3 + 2Mu^3.$$

Solving this for $d\phi$, we find

$$d\phi = \frac{du}{\sqrt{2M(u^3 - u_0^3) - (u^2 - u_0^2)}}.$$

If we introduce a new variable x through the relation

$$u = u_0 \sin x,$$

and, after the substitution, develop according to powers of M, retaining only two terms, we obtain the following approximate expression for

$$\left(1 + Mu_0 \frac{1 - \sin^3 x}{1 - \sin^2 x}\right) dx.$$

Now, if we let x change from zero to π, u will change from zero to u_0 and back to zero. This is just the change that the inverse distance will experience during the propagation of the light particle. The total change of the angle will then be represented by the integral

$$\int_0^\pi \left[1 + Mu_0 \frac{1 - \sin^3 x}{1 - \sin^2 x}\right] dx.$$

In the old theory the term with M in this integral is missing so that the result is π. The approximate result according to the new theory will differ from this by

$$Mu_0 \int_0^\pi \frac{1 - \sin^3 x}{1 - \sin^2 x}\, dx = Mu_0 \left[\tan\left(\frac{x}{2} - \frac{\pi}{4}\right) - \cos x\right]_0^\pi = 4Mu_0.$$

The beam of light coming to us from a star will therefore be deflected by an angle $4M/r_0$ (where r_0 is its minimum distance from the sun) from its value given by the old theory, or from the direction of the beam if the sun were absent. If then we observe a star in a certain position on the sky while the sun is far away, and then observe the same star when the sun is near the line of vision (i.e., when the apparent position of the sun is near the apparent position of the star), this latter position must appear shifted away from the sun by the angle $4M/r_0$, approximately. Actual measurements are possible only during an eclipse of the sun, because otherwise the light from the sun drowns out the fainter light from the star, and even then are beset with difficulties, but the results seem to be in favor of this prediction.

37. Shift of spectral lines

We come to the third so-called test of the general relativity theory; we shall discuss still another situation where the predictions of the theory differ from those of older theories by an amount exceeding the error of measurement, thus affording an opportunity to prove or disprove the advantages of the new theory.

Here again we deal with propagation of light in the gravitational field of the sun, but this time the source is supposed to be on the sun itself, and the observer is on the earth, so that the direction of the beam is that of a radius of the sun. We interpret this to mean that θ = constant and ϕ = constant. We have then according to 33.5, with $A = 0$,

37.1 $$\frac{\dot{r}^2}{\eta} - \eta \dot{t}^2 = 0.$$

This gives

$$dr = \pm \eta \, dt,$$

where the double sign corresponds to two possible senses of the beam: from the sun to the earth, and from the earth to the sun. The former, in which we are now interested, is characterized by the property that r increases as t increases, and the ratio dr/dt must therefore be positive. Since η is positive we must take

37.2 $$dr = \eta \, dt.$$

The orbit is thus determined by the equations

$$d\theta = 0, \qquad d\phi = 0, \qquad dr = \eta \, dt.$$

But this time we are interested in the color or frequency, which, as was shown in section 17, is proportional to the time component of the momentum vector. As the momentum vector we have to consider the vector of components dx^i/dp, where p is the parameter appearing in the equations of geodesics with respect to which differentiation is denoted by $\cdot$. In order to determine this parameter we have to go back to the original equations of geodesics. Now 33.21 becomes

$$\ddot{r} - \frac{\eta'}{2\eta} \cdot \dot{r}^2 + \frac{\eta\eta'}{2} \cdot \dot{t}^2 = 0,$$

and equation 37.1 shows that the last two terms cancel, so that

$$\ddot{r} = 0.$$

This means that r is a linear function of the parameter

$$r = ap + b,$$

so that

$$\frac{d}{dp} = a \frac{d}{dr}.$$

The components of the momentum vector $\dot{x}^i$ are therefore

$$a \frac{dr}{dr} = a, \qquad a \frac{d\theta}{dr} = 0, \qquad a \frac{d\phi}{dr} = 0, \qquad a \frac{dt}{dr} = \frac{a}{\eta},$$

where the last relation follows from 37.2.   What about the value of
a?   The answer is that it is not and cannot be determined by the
foregoing discussion.   There are different beams of light that satisfy
all the conditions imposed so far.   They differ in *color* or frequency,
and different colors correspond to different values of a.

Frequencies, according to section 17, are equal to the time components of the momentum vector, i.e., the inner product of the momentum vector of light and the unit vector in the time direction.   If we
denote the (contravariant) components of the latter by T^i, the condition that it has time direction will be given by

$$T^1 = T^2 = T^3 = 0,$$

and the condition that it is a unit vector by

$$g_{ij} T^i T^j = -1.$$

If the preceding relations and the values of the g's are used, this
becomes

$$\eta (T^4)^2 = 1.$$

The inner product of the vectors $\dot{x}^i$ and T^i calculated according to
the formula $g_{ij} \dot{x}^i T^j$ is

$$\eta \frac{a}{\eta} \eta^{-\frac{1}{2}} = a \left(1 - \frac{2M}{r} \right)^{-\frac{1}{2}},$$

or, if we expand and keep only the first two terms,

$$a \left(1 + \frac{M}{r} \right).$$

The frequency of a beam of light is therefore not constant along the
beam.   We shall compare the frequency as it appears near the surface
of the sun, where r is equal to the radius of the sun r_s, and near the
surface of the earth, where we may assume $r = \infty$.   For a given beam
of light the frequencies in these two cases will be proportional to

$$1 + \frac{M}{r_s} \quad \text{and} \quad 1.$$

The change in frequency therefore will be proportional to

$$\left(1 + \frac{M}{r_s} \right) - 1 = \frac{M}{r_s},$$

and this also will be the relative change in frequency.

If now we consider some source of light near the surface of the sun, whose frequency we know, the light emitted by it when it is received at the surface of the earth will have a frequency that is *less*, the amount of the relative change being given by M/r_s.

If then we compare light coming from a terrestrial source, as, for example, that emitted by an atom, and light emitted by a corresponding source on the sun, for example, that emitted by an atom of the same kind, we would expect a change of frequency of the amount M/r_s. Of, if we compare a solar spectrum with a terrestrial spectrum, the lines of the former will be shifted toward the red by the amount M/r_s. This is the prediction of the general relativity theory.

Again the experimental evidence seems to favor this prediction.

CONCLUSION

In the preceding pages, two types of propositions, mathematical and physical, were not separated from each other. This procedure was followed, as mentioned in the Preface, in order to make it easier for the reader to enter into the subject. But now that the theory has been introduced, it seems desirable to try to make clear in a few words the spirit in which application of mathematics to physics is understood. *In principle* it is possible to separate the two types of propositions from each other. We may say that the text consists of two parts although the propositions constituting these two parts are intermingled. The propositions of the first type deal with axioms, definitions, assumptions, and theorems and their derivations. Some of these propositions are stated in words, and some in mathematical symbolism, in formulas and equations involving certain mathematical quantities. These mathematical quantities are identified in the propositions of the second type with quantities discussed in books on physics and astronomy. This identification makes a physical theory of the mathematical propositions. As the result of this identification the mathematical propositions and formulas may be interpreted as relations between the measured quantities of physics. If these relations coincide (within experimental errors) with relations which appear to be accepted by physicists and astronomers we say that these last relations, or the experimental and observational facts expressed by them, are *explained* on the basis of the mathematical theory; in some cases when the relations stated in the formulas have not been observed prior to their derivation, but *are* observed after, we speak of predictions that have been verified. In both cases we speak of confirmation of the theory of observation.

This in the author's opinion is the nature of application of mathematics to physics. It is not asserted that there always exists a theory explaining all the facts, and it is not denied that there may exist at the same time two theories which explain (within the experimental errors) the known facts equally well. Thus neither uniqueness nor existence is claimed for a mathematical theory of physical phenomena. In this respect it differs from the concept of truth held by some people. The question whether there is such a thing as truth—questions of the type "What does actually happen?" questions about "physical reality"—we do not consider in this book.

INDEX

Numbers refer to pages unless otherwise indicated

171